6-22-22
7-27-22

HAPPY BIRTHDAY
Jim!

ENJOY THE JOURNEY

Larry

LARRY

Enjoy the Read

Maggie

INDENTURED

A Pathway to America

LARRY AND MAGGIE KESSLER

ISBN: 978-1-953058-12-6

Printed in the United States of America

Book design by Scott Stortz

Published by:
Butler Books
(502) 897–9393
info@butlerbooks.com
www.butlerbooks.com

This book is dedicated to all the men, women, and children who came to this country as indentured servants, seeking a better life.

Their efforts and sacrifice helped give us the luxury to live in this great land.

CONTENTS

PART TWO

Introduction

From the early 1600s through the end of the American Revolution, one-half to two-thirds of the laborers who came to America were indentured servants. Indentured servants were men and women who signed contracts known as indentures or covenants, in which they agreed to work for a certain number of years in exchange for transportation to America. Upon their arrival, food, clothing, and shelter were provided. For adults, the contracts were generally four to seven years. For children, they were much longer; children, no matter their ages at the time their contracts were signed, were required to serve until they were twenty-one.

Some indentured servants came to America as families, but mostly they were young men around the age of twenty-one, the legal age of majority in many places at that time. Many teenage boys also became indentured; typically, the father of a teenager would sign the legal papers.

Some early indentured servants were recruited to ships by "Neulanders" or "New Worlders," men who had served their time as indentures and now worked as recruiters. They were decked out in fancy attire and received a commission for each person recruited.

Many of these early recruits, most of them from Britain and Germany, were used in the tobacco fields, where there was an inexhaustible need for labor. Lured by promises of riches in the New World, they flooded the colonies.

Unfortunately, those promises were largely false. For instance, families who had been assured they would stay together often found upon arrival that they had been indentured to different masters. Wives were separated from husbands and children from their parents, perhaps never to see one another again. They were also greeted by deadly diseases and harsh conditions that killed a majority of newcomers and left the rest to the mercy of masters who were often cruel.

It was a difficult life; indentured servants worked long hours and were often mistreated, beaten, and sexually abused by their masters. Women and children were especially abused. They "died like cats and dogs," according to the Dutchman David DeVries, who visited the colonies in 1633. He reported on how some servants were lost through gambling and taken by other masters, saying, "I told them I had never seen such work in Turk or Barbarian . . ."

Some indentured servants were trapped in seemingly endless servitude. They were often fooled by sea merchants who would offer them free passage but would charge them a steep fare when they arrived. Prospective masters would then pay the fare and bargain with the immigrants directly to determine how many years of labor would be required to pay the debt. Having already arrived in America, these immigrants were at a great disadvantage; they had no other options, and many spent years longer in servitude than they had expected to.

"Redemptioners," most of them from Germany, had perhaps the

hardest time. Their contracts were sold to the captains of the ships that brought them to America. Redemptioners were at the mercy of the types of contracts the captains could arrange once in America. Sometimes ships would have to sail on before the passengers could be sold; in that case, an agent would confine the immigrants until someone came to purchase them. Sometimes months went by, and many died while waiting.

Indentured servitude was the method of choice for planters looking for laborers in the early days of the American colonies. And while the enslavement of Africans was more common than indentured servitude in the eighteenth and early nineteenth centuries, the practice of indentured servitude continued, lasting until the early twentieth century. While indentured servitude could be brutal, it cannot be compared to chattel slavery. At least indentured servants knew that they—or at least their descendants—would be free someday, although for many, "someday" was a very long time away. When indentured servants and enslaved people, who often lived in the same quarters, had children together, these biracial children could be sentenced to thirty years of servitude.

What follows is the story of one family that contracted with an unscrupulous Neulander, only to discover that almost nothing he had told them was true.

EVIL IN KENTUCKY, SUMMER 1838

Mattie woke as usual before it was light, ready to do her chores. Baby William was still asleep as she quietly dressed for the day. When she entered the kitchen, there sat her father Daniel, silently enjoying his first cup of coffee.

As Mattie fixed the morning meal, she heard young Will stirring. She fetched him and seated him next to his grandfather, who dearly loved this little redheaded boy of two. Daniel had already given Mattie one of his most precious possessions, his grandfather Johann's army knife, to pass along to Will when he was old enough.

As they breakfasted together, Daniel and Mattie talked about what was to be done on the farm that day. Mattie, as usual, was full of happy chatter while Daniel, a man of few words, mostly smiled and nodded.

The day proceeded as usual, except for one thing . . . Mattie's secret.

In the afternoon, Mattie told Daniel that she would be spending the night at the home of her mother-in-law, Lucinda White, after they attended a prayer service. They were going to make the year's fruit preserves, she said; it would take a few days. Mattie's husband, William White, would not be there. He had never been happy in Kentucky and had decided several months earlier to go to Alabama in search of work. He had promised to return soon for his wife and child, but he had not. He had not even sent a letter home.

Having distant family members in Alabama, Lucinda and her other two sons had decided to move there as well and had asked Mattie to come with them. She had been torn between going with the Whites and staying with her father, who very much needed her help. He, in turn, was vehemently against her traveling with a young child all the way to Alabama. Daniel had never liked or approved of William, and he thought both Mattie and young Will would be better off without him.

At first, Mattie had decided to go to Alabama. She wanted to be with her husband again, and she wanted her son to grow up with a father.

However, Mattie had not had the courage to tell Daniel of her decision, so she and Lucinda had made a plan for Mattie to come to Lucinda's house that day. They would make final preparations for the trip and then wait until evening, when the men they'd hired to move them to Alabama would come in the dark of night. Then they could quietly leave town without anyone knowing.

But on this day, after the prayer service, Mattie told her mother-in-law that she had changed her mind and would not be going. If William wanted his wife and child, he could come to Kentucky for them. She was not going to make the long journey and break her father's heart to chase after a man who did not want her. Also, she privately agreed with her father's assessment that the men who were organizing the move were untrustworthy and possibly even dangerous.

Mattie told Lucinda she was on her way to the home of Carrington Simpson, the man who was organizing the Whites' move, to let him know she and Will would not be going after all.

As Mattie and Will rode up to Simpson's farm on her horse, Good Fellow, she saw Simpson standing by the packed oxcart. Looking at his cold eyes and cruel half-smile made her shudder. She was certain she had made the right decision in refusing to go anywhere with him . . .

PART ONE

CHAPTER 1

THE DECISION

In 1746, when Ulrich Kessler was ten years old, his father Johann decided that the family would leave their homeland and journey to America. In their small community in the German territory of Baden, near the French border, farming had become impossible, and war had devastated the land and might do so again. Many families had already left.

Johann convinced his wife Matilda and daughter Hannah that going to this new country would give them a fresh start and many new opportunities. They were excited to be on this new adventure. Ulrich, however, was not so sure. He was reluctant to leave, even when the house, animals, and acreage had all been sold.

The night before the family's departure, Matilda and Hannah were in the kitchen preparing a special meal, including each person's favorite dish. More than likely, this would be their last hot meal for a while. As the smells from the kitchen permeated the house, Johann helped his son decide what to pack. Ulrich was not being very cooperative, and before long he started begging again.

"Please, Papa, I want to stay here," he said. "I don't want to make the long journey to a new country. This is my home."

"Ulrich, I'm doing what is best for the family," Johann said. "We are barely surviving here. This new country is a land full of opportunity. We must try to better ourselves. You are old enough to understand that this is what we must do. I know leaving our home is not easy, but life here has become so difficult that we have no choice.

"Perhaps, if I tell you a secret, you will feel better about leaving. But you must promise not to say anything to Hannah or Mama. It is to be a surprise after we arrive in Rotterdam. Until then, this will be our secret, just between the two of us."

"Papa, please tell me," Ulrich said. "I am good at keeping secrets."

"All right. Your mother has always wanted you and Hannah to attend school. She asked for my promise that I would arrange it if it were possible. I have done so, and you can both attend for as long as we are in Rotterdam; as you know, it may take weeks or months for me to secure our passage to America. You know I always keep my promises, especially to Mama."

"Papa," Ulrich said, "I can hardly wait to get to Rotterdam and go to a real school! Mama has been a good teacher, teaching us our numbers and how to read and write, but now we can learn even more. Thank you, Papa. I won't forget it's our secret, just between the two of us."

With that, the redheaded boy with freckles on his nose embraced his Papa. Mama received most of the hugs; Johann would treasure this one for a long time.

CHAPTER 2

MATILDA'S PREPARATIONS

The day before leaving when the house was empty, Matilda realized it was a perfect time to go through the house and make decisions about personal items. It was going to be difficult; this was the only home she had ever known. Although rather small, it was comfortable and had been well taken care of and loved. Johann had excellent carpentry skills and had made sure everything was repaired and in good working order. Because of him, the land, house, and animals had brought a good price. She smiled as she looked at the large table he had built so that she could prepare meals more easily and at the extra shelving he had installed for her dried herbs and seeds. All the furniture had been skillfully fixed, lasting longer than it should have. Everything Johann had done had helped to improve the property. Her father had been right about him when he'd said, "Johann is a good man."

It was now time to go through the top drawer of the old chest that Matilda's father had left her. It was filled with her parents' personal papers. Most would be thrown into the fireplace to burn; only important papers concerning the land and house would be saved.

She was briefly looking at and then discarding the pages until she found a piece of yellowing paper with her name and "age eight" at the top. It was a poem she had written as a little girl.

Little rabbit . . . hopping around . . . stop . . .

Canopy above . . . providing safety . . . be at peace . . .

Slowdown heartbeat . . . look around . . .

There is no sound . . . you will not be found . . .

As she stood there remembering the little girl who had written the poem, tears came to her eyes, one running down her cheek; she wiped her face as she tasted the salty tears. She leaned on the old dresser, wondering once again whether they were doing the right thing by leaving this place. She folded the paper and placed it in the pocket of her dress, to be read again someday.

She gathered herself together and again started moving through the house. There were so many good memories; both she and her children had been born here. She could only hope there would be more happy memories made in their new home. It was hard to imagine America being more beautiful than the big sky, hills, and valleys of the land she knew and loved, with her favorite color, green, all around. And she would miss the trips to the nearby village of Kehl, especially the annual harvest festival, where everyone knew one another and all were welcomed. Their neighbors were kind and were always willing to help when help was needed.

She couldn't help but wonder: would her family find all of this in the new country?

CHAPTER 3

The Last Night at Home

The night before their departure, they shared a special meal. There was little talking at first, except to tell Matilda how much they appreciated her cooking for them. They all knew how much effort and preparation had gone into making this meal special.

As they all sat full, content, and happy, she had a request: "I would like for each of you to tell me what you will miss the most and what you look forward to once we arrive in America."

Ulrich and Johann thought this was silly and didn't respond, but Hannah said, "Oh, this will be fun!"

"I will start," Matilda said, "and then Papa, Hannah, and Ulrich will take their turns.

"This land and house are all I have ever known. I was born here, married here, raised my two beautiful children here. I have never traveled more than a few hours away. Now I will be going on a journey so much farther than I could have ever imagined. Above all, I think I will miss the land and my garden. All that can be replaced, but what I take with me can't be. What I take with me really is the most important thing, and that is the three of you. We will take our memories and make new memories together as a family.

"I have already started planning my new garden in America. I never tire of seeing the looks on the faces of you children when you see the first green tips peeking out of the ground; Hannah, I remember you telling me once that they looked almost like little people exploring their new world. Soon they grow and grow, becoming nourishment for all of us.

"It is now your turn, Johann."

"I think I was the luckiest man in the world when I came to work here and met you, Matilda—the best cook in all the world!—whom I married," Johann said. "Then we were blessed with two children. Like your mother, I will miss the land and especially the garden, the one I promised her would be the envy of everyone. Now, your turn, Hannah."

"I will miss all my secret hiding places," Hannah said. "I would go to them when I was trying to have private time away from my little brother, but of course he would usually find me. When we are on our journey, I will miss Mama's cooking, like the special meal she made tonight. I especially loved the dessert tonight; Mama, the phannkuchen were delicious. The dough was so soft and sweet and the jelly inside was *mmmm*, so good. Tomorrow we will begin our great adventure, seeing new places, meeting new people . . . how exciting!

"Your turn," she said as she smiled and turned to Ulrich.

"I will miss everything," Ulrich said. "Helping Papa with chores and Mama with her garden and her cooking. Letting Hannah think she was hiding from me. The animals, the land, the house. Everything. I wish we didn't have to leave, except that when we arrive in Rotterdam I'm going to be able to—"

Not a moment too soon, Johann chimed in, "Ulrich and I are planning on doing some serious fishing there. It is something we can do together. Right, Ulrich?"

"Yes, Papa," Ulrich said, as he became aware that Papa had saved the day. The stern look Papa gave him could have frozen a lake over. But the great secret keeper had not spoiled the surprise . . . at least, not yet.

Matilda could see that everyone was tired. It was time to end the evening. As she and Hannah started clearing the table, she instructed Ulrich and Johann to go to bed.

"We need a good night's sleep," Matilda reminded them. "Our journey starts in the morning."

CHAPTER 4

THE JOURNEY BEGINS

It seemed that they had hardly slept when Hannah shook Ulrich and said, "Get up! Papa and Mama are already eating breakfast. Go quickly and get a biscuit while they're hot. I will finish the packing."

There was little to pack, only what each person could carry. Johann, as the strongest, carried most of the pots, pans, and cooking utensils, along with the blankets.

The trip down the Rhine was made on the *Alfred*, a rectangular flatboat with sails, ideal for river voyages. At two hundred feet long and thirty-five across, it was spacious, but most of the space was dedicated to cargo. The rest was taken up by emigrating families like the Kesslers.

The five-day trip was fairly enjoyable and uneventful, except when Johann had to pay the tariffs and taxes. His main worry was that they would run out of money before he could secure a job. However, Hannah and Ulrich had no worries, and before long, they had made friends with other children on the boat. Matilda made conversation with other women and gathered information about Rotterdam from those who knew the city. She was told about several places the family might rent. One was near the docks, where Johann was hoping to find work. They would go there first.

Arriving at the port city was at first overwhelming, more so than they had ever imagined. But they had no time to waste. Following the directions Matilda had been given, they soon found their way down a quiet street. Standing in front of number four, Johann knocked on the door. An elderly woman opened it and greeted them.

"My name is Johann Kessler, and this is my family. We are here to inquire about the room for rent," Johann said.

"Nice to meet all of you. I am Greta, and I would be happy to show you what I have; just follow me. The room is behind the house. It was my husband's office when he was alive. I have no need or use for the space, so I rent it out for extra income. I require a full month's rent in advance and would like two weeks' notice upon leaving. As you can see, the room has its own entrance, which will give your family more privacy."

They entered the room. There was not much to observe: four cots, a table with four chairs, a table by the fireplace to prepare food on, and a broom standing by the door.

Matilda could tell by the look on Johann's face that he'd expected more. Johann was about to express his disappointment when she spoke first.

"Greta, I think this will work out just fine; it suits our needs at this time. And look at all the beautiful light coming from not one, but two, windows. We will have a wonderful breeze on these hot days. Also, I will be able to grow some herbs on the windowsills and—with your permission, Greta—make curtains for the windows."

Nothing more was said. The decision had been made. Johann handed over the first month's rent. Greta, smiling, left and shut the door behind her.

Johann hugged his wife and thanked her for being so accommodating, for never complaining and always supporting him.

He would start looking for work in the morning.

CHAPTER 5

ROTTERDAM

After several rejections and many signs that read "No help needed," Johann was feeling dejected. He was walking along the docks toward their room, his head hung down and shoulders slumped, when someone called out to him.

"You there, are you looking for work?"

Johann looked up to see a grizzled man.

"Yes, sir, I am," Johann said. "I will do anything you need."

"Have you ever worked on a dock before?" the man asked.

"No, sir, but I am strong, and I am a very hard worker. I will not let you down."

"All right. I will give you a try. You can start right now; one of my men didn't show up this morning, probably had too much rum last night. If you can't keep up, though, I'll have to let you go."

Johann had not eaten anything and was very hungry, but he knew he had to start right then.

"Thank you, sir. I will work hard for you."

That night was a happy time.

It did not take long for the Kessler family to adjust to life in Rotterdam. Johann's job on the docks went well, and he enjoyed all the activity around the harbor. He especially liked seeing the ships come in and all the commotion they caused. He was amazed at the amount of cargo just one ship could carry. Ulrich was fascinated too; after school and on Saturdays, he would often take lunch or a hot drink to his father and observe life at the docks. He also helped Johann with his work just so they could both get home more quickly, much to Matilda's delight.

Certainly, the work was hard. Johann returned home most days with sore shoulders and swollen hands from all the cargo he'd unloaded that day. However, he did not complain; it was no harder than farming, and he was working toward his goal.

Both Ulrich and Hannah loved exploring Rotterdam with their newfound friends, and they loved attending school. Matilda was extremely proud when Ulrich told her that the headmaster had been impressed with their progress and with all they had learned at home before starting school. Matilda was quick to give the credit to her parents.

"They insisted I become an educated person," she told Ulrich. "I had no choice. But I loved learning. Father taught me writing, mathematics, and history. But it was Mother who inspired me to see and understand the world around me. Mother loved gardening and all of nature; she made sure I would love it as well.

"When I was a young child, she asked me questions about how I saw the world, and she always listened attentively to my answers. For instance, once she asked me what I liked best about the garden, and I said I loved to see the plants growing bigger each day just as I was growing bigger each day. I also told her how I liked to go out into the garden after it had rained. The air smelled so clean, and in my mind, nature was giving everything a drink and a bath at the same time. My mother said, 'You are very observant for a little girl of four.'"

Even though Matilda could not have a garden in Rotterdam, she did grow herbs on the windowsills, and she did make curtains for the windows. She also started caring for an elderly neighbor a few hours each day. She used the extra money to purchase food items for the voyage.

She also purchased a small book that translated common German words and phrases into English. She insisted that they all practice learning the new words. Her enthusiasm was infectious, and so every night after the evening meal they all practiced the funny-sounding words, laughing at one another and especially at Johann, who made funny faces after every new word. To Matilda's delight, Ulrich was always especially eager to play the new word game. Neither of them had any way of knowing that the little phrasebook would one day become one of Ulrich's most treasured belongings.

One evening, Johann arrived home later than usual.

"Matilda, I finally met the man who can help us. His name is Harvey Suter. He is signing up people who want free passage to America and who are willing to work for a few years under what is called an indentured contract. We can all enter into the contract and travel together."

Johann showed much enthusiasm, but secretly he was hesitant. All was going very well in Rotterdam; maybe this was where the family should make their new home. In the end, though, his dreams about America prevailed.

CHAPTER 6

THE CONTRACT

Even though Johann had not yet spoken to Harvey Suter again, Matilda started making plans for the voyage. She gathered staples such as coffee, tea, cured meats, cheese, dried beans, spices, and some medicinal herbs that she had grown. When the time came for departure, she would bake the perishables, and these would be eaten first.

When she had done all she could to prepare for the trip, she wondered, *How much longer?*

Soon, though, Johann met with Suter again. Johann knew little about indenture, and Suter was well-spoken on the subject. According to Suter, Johann would have a good job waiting for him in America, and when his indenture was finished, he would be given land, tools, money, and a year's supply of corn. He would be a wealthy man then. It all sounded so good that Johann practically begged Suter to sign him up. However, Suter was cagey and told Johann that he would have to wait his turn. This was a ploy to get Johann to sign anything Suter put in front of him.

Several weeks went by while Suter promised Johann a contract soon.

Then, one day early in May, Suter came to the wharf to tell Johann, "Mr. Kessler, I have good news for you. A farmer in Pennsylvania would like to hire you. You must be ready to sail on the *Webb* by the twenty-eighth of May. Will that be suitable for you and your family?"

"Yes," replied Johann. "They will be excited, as they have been waiting for this news for some time."

And, just as Suter had thought he would, Johann signed the contract.

When Johann arrived home that evening, he was laughing. He seized Matilda, lifted her off the ground, and spun her around.

"Johann, what is it?" Matilda exclaimed in an excited voice.

Johann then gathered Ulrich and Hannah close to him.

"We will be celebrating your birthday in two weeks," he told Matilda, "and we will be doing it on the ship to America."

Johann pulled the children even closer. Matilda joined them and they all hugged as a warm, loving family. All agreed that May twenty-eighth was the perfect day to set sail.

Had he known the full meaning of the term "indentured," Johann would never have agreed to sign the contract. He was only interested in securing passage for his family to America. He did not know that his family would be considered the property of their masters or that they could be sold to pay off debts. He did not know that, under some circumstances, their descendants could also be sold or inherited. Human chattel, like other property, were governed largely by state laws, which favored employers.

In Johann's case, his family's indenture contract would be sold to the captain of the *Webb*, a man named Bradford, who had connections with several indenture employers in America. Most of them were farm owners needing cheap labor.

CHAPTER 7

Boarding the Ship

The family had not slept well the night before the departure, being too excited and anxious about the trip. As always, Matilda assured everyone that they would be fine. Her enthusiasm for the adventure was infectious. That night she helped the family pack their bags, placing food items between articles of clothing. Only one bag or suitcase was allotted per family member; any more would be left on the wharf. Johann had assured her that, according to Mr. Suter, plenty of food would be supplied for the voyage, with each person receiving a weekly ration. But Matilda was not taking any chances.

When the twenty-eighth came, they left their rented room in the early hours of the morning. After months of planning, the day had finally arrived. Since it was not far to the docks, they were soon standing in line to board the *Webb*.

They were all anxious. Though the weather could not have been more perfect—May was the best time of the year to set sail—none of them had ever been on a large ship on the open ocean before. In addition to their concerns about the dangers of any sea voyage, they were worried about seasickness, about which they'd heard many stories. But Matilda assured Johann and the children that she had something to give them if they felt ill, and those who had sailed before said that their bodies would soon adjust to the movement of the ship, as long as the weather was good and they did not hit large swells.

Soon the line began to move, and the Kesslers reached the deck. The first crew member they saw there was the captain's first mate. His name, they were told, was Red Jack. He was short and stocky, with dark eyes and skin that looked like leather from many years at sea. His red hair, though thinning and matted, was blowing in the wind, like flames shooting out the top of his head, and the areas around his cheekbones resembled two tomatoes.

Ulrich had seen many men like Red Jack around the docks, rough-looking men whom he didn't want to know. Now he and Matilda felt uneasy as Red Jack's eyes lingered longer on Hannah than they should have. If they had known about his true character, they might have turned and abandoned the ship immediately, but they did not know, and anyway, it was too late. The ship was sailing.

Passengers were now being given orders to go below deck to store belongings and to secure sleeping quarters for the duration of the voyage. With nearly four hundred passengers, there wasn't much room below. Each space allotted was only two feet by six feet; passengers would be stacked along the walls of the ship, packed in densely like herrings. Around them were stored tools, provisions, and water barrels, making the crowding worse. There was no privacy; all would be sleeping and eating in the same place.

Before long, another ship's mate ordered them to a section of the hold where there was a kitchen area for cooking and warming food. It was called the "cookshop" and was a small area, only six by twelve feet. There was barely enough room for one person, much less for several to be cooking at the same time. Matilda looked at Johann with a question on her face; how could this be the only cooking area? Johann did not respond, as they were now being ordered to go on deck, where Red Jack would be giving instructions on the ship's rules.

The rules were read as follows:
1. No wandering around the ship without permission.
2. Food and provisions will be provided once per week. They will consist of oatmeal, biscuits, flour, two pounds of rice, one-half pound of sugar, one-half pound of molasses, and two ounces of tea.
3. Fighting and/or stealing will be dealt with harshly, at the captain's discretion.
4. Each family is responsible for taking care of its own sick members.
5. The "cookshop" is on a first-come, first-served basis.
6. The captain's and crew's quarters are off-limits to passengers.
7. Passengers must ask permission to come up on deck.
8. If death occurs on the journey, the body will be buried at sea.
9. All guns must be turned in and will be returned at the end of the voyage.
10. The ship has no formal prayer service during the voyage, but passengers may hold one on Sundays and at funerals.

As Jack finished barking out his instructions, other crew members started handing out chamber pots, with instructions on how passengers were responsible for disposing of their own waste each day through the large porthole in the hold.

Several hours had passed, and the coastline of Rotterdam was disappearing into the horizon. There was excitement as the realization dawned on the passengers that they were truly heading to a new land. The adventure had begun. Passengers mingled, making new acquaintances, the children gravitating to one another as children always do, playing and making up games.

Soon the sun was setting, and orders came to go below. It had been a long day, and most were ready for nourishment and sleep. Matilda started setting out the food she had prepared back in their rented room; however, the family noticed she seemed weary and was not moving as she usually did. They tried to help, but she shooed them away.

Then, to their surprise, she proceeded to pull up her dress. There, hanging from her waist, were links of dried sausage. As they watched, she also pulled two blocks of cheese from her underskirt. And there was more to come, as she showed the family how she had sewn dried beans and medicinal herbs into the hems of her dress and undergarments.

It was when Matilda unbuttoned the top of her dress and four biscuits fell out that they started laughing so hard that tears were running down their cheeks. Before long they were all having a good laugh, even Matilda, realizing how funny she must have looked.

That was the best night on the ship; they never laughed that way again during the voyage.

CHAPTER 8

RED JACK ENCOUNTER

After a few days aboard the ship, the family learned why the crew referred to it as the "Porker Stern," meaning "Pig's Ass." It was because of the foul odor from human waste, illness, body odor, and rotten food that permeated everything belowdecks.

But even more foul, if that were possible, was Red Jack. He chewed tobacco almost continuously, and his breath was testament to that. When he laughed—generally cruelly—his teeth showed brown and yellow like elephant tusks. But the passengers were more concerned about his lack of character; he seemed to care little for anyone other than himself. He maneuvered around the ship growling and barking out orders to both crew and passengers. Worst of all, he was known to have his way with the women on board, sometimes with willing wives in return for food for their families and sometimes with young maidens who were unwilling.

The Kesslers learned that Jack had also indentured himself, years before, to pay for a prison sentence. His indenture had also been with Captain Bradford, a decent man but one who expected all parties to live up to their contracts. Jack had tried to leave the ship upon his arrival in America, before he could be sold, but Captain Bradford had caught up with him and brought him back to the ship, where he was flogged.

Afterward, the captain had given Jack two options: "You can either go back to prison or serve on the *Webb* for four voyages to America at no pay. At the end of the last voyage, you will be sold to fulfill your original contract."

Red Jack had accepted these terms and was now on his third voyage.

When the ship stopped in London, Hannah and Ulrich first encountered the drunken Red Jack. When in port, the crew would go ashore at night to visit taverns and prostitutes, leaving the upper deck for passengers to roam about. Hannah and Ulrich were sitting on the deck late one night, after Matilda and Johann were asleep, when several crew members came aboard. They were noisy, laughing, telling stories of the "wenches" they had been with that night and singing songs of the sea. They passed a bottle of rum and sang raucously:

No glory I covet, no riches I want,

Ambition is nothing to me,

The one thing I beg of kind heaven to grant

Is a mind independent and free . . .

Hannah and Ulrich were quiet at the other end of the deck, listening. Then Red Jack drunkenly stumbled their way. They sat frozen like two mice being stalked by a cat, unable to move, hoping he wouldn't see them. But he did, and he leaned in close to them.

"You go below, boy, and leave me with your sister. We need to get better acquainted," Jack leered, slurring his words and spewing brown spit. His breath smelled like a mixture of tobacco, rum, and garlic; it made them gag. Before they could react, he had seized Hannah, wrapping his thick arms around her. Ulrich could tell that she was terrified and unable to move.

Even though Ulrich feared Red Jack, as did everyone on board, he had made a promise to Matilda and to himself to look after his sister and keep her safe. It was in that instant, with the thought of protecting her, that he made his move. Jack had put down his bottle of rum in order to free his hands to do as he pleased. Ulrich grabbed the bottle and hit Jack across the shin. Jack let go of Hannah, and Ulrich grabbed her hand and pulled her to the hatch, where they scurried down the ladder.

Above them, they heard Jack moaning and cursing. They just sat there, holding each other and vowing never to tell their parents what had happened.

For days, they worried that Red Jack would come looking for them, but he never did. Ulrich had kept his sister safe. Unfortunately, they both knew others hadn't been so lucky.

CHAPTER 9

The Voyage Continues

The *Webb* stayed in London for much longer than the passengers had anticipated; the ship docked for eight days, waiting for cargo to be loaded. Johann was able to work a few days for extra food rations, mainly "captain's biscuits," which were large, round slabs of baked dough. When fresh, they were tasty. However, the ones Johann was given were stale and hard, full of worms and spiders' nests; only about half of each could be eaten. Matilda would pull the good portions off and warm them on the hot stove. They were still stale, but warm and with a little molasses, they became tolerable and helped extend the supplies.

Unless given permission to work on the docks, the passengers were not allowed to leave the ship while it was in port, but while the crew were ashore, passengers were allowed on deck. Most of their time was spent there, making the most of the fresh air and sunshine at last. The adults who were not working elsewhere did chores, washing clothes, sewing, and preparing food. The children spent some time on English lessons, but mostly they played, much to Matilda's delight.

Hannah and Ulrich often played games together, but it was always more fun when they could get others to join in. The children would run the length of the ship, racing and watching the birds land and take off again.

All the passengers would stay on deck as long as possible each day. Only when ordered to by the crew would everyone go below.

Finally, the *Webb* left London and headed out into the Atlantic, where things took a turn for the worse. In these rougher waters, many suffered from the nausea and dizziness of seasickness. Below decks, passengers lay in their bunks, unable to move around; it was quiet except for the miserable sounds of vomiting. People would vomit into their family waste pots and leave them full until morning; the stench was becoming more and more intolerable.

The Kessler family was faring better than most. The herbs Matilda had brought, they agreed, were "God sent"; she brewed them into a tea, and each family member enjoyed the benefits.

After the seasickness subsided, things were tolerable for a while. However, soon many passengers were sick with fever. Some were covered with boils and lice. Little time was given to go above for fresh air and sunshine, and the stench grew even worse.

By the fourth week, things were starting to become bleak. The passengers were becoming irritable, and tempers were boiling. Most of the food they had brought aboard was now gone, and they were forced to eat the food supplied by the ship's crew—food so salty it was not fit to eat—and drink water that became more brackish and contaminated by the day.

By the following week, things were even worse. The arguing and fighting among the passengers were escalating, which only exacerbated the already horrible conditions. Disease was rampant; each day only brought more misery. Soon, people began dying and were quickly removed and tossed into the sea, with no real funeral services, only a few words spoken. Sleep became the only escape from this moving hellhole. Like a mother hen, Matilda kept the family close and away from others and their sickness.

Soon, though, another passenger was in need of Matilda's care. All below took notice when the passengers heard a woman screaming and crying for help. Miss Katherine Shaughnessy, who was traveling alone, was in labor. She had no husband and had not disclosed to the captain when she indentured herself that she was nearly seven months pregnant. She had thought she would be in America before the baby arrived. But now, five weeks later, the baby was coming early.

Matilda went right to Katherine, explaining that she had delivered a few babies and would do everything she could to help. She headed to the kitchen for hot water and ordered Hannah and Ulrich to try to comfort Katherine, who was in terrible pain, screaming until she passed out. Then the contractions would start again and bring on more screaming. Other women came to help, but Katherine, who had been battling dysentery for weeks, was just too weak; her body went limp and all screaming stopped. When Matilda returned, she could find no pulse. Katherine Shaughnessy was dead.

But Matilda didn't know whether the baby was still alive; perhaps it could be saved. She told Ulrich to find Red Jack and bring him quickly. He came grudgingly, spitting and swearing the whole way. Matilda explained the situation and pleaded with Jack to let her take

Katherine's body to the ship's infirmary, where a crewman, though not a doctor, sometimes treated ill or injured crew members.

"The infirmary is for the crew; we have no provisions for women giving birth," Jack replied. "Besides, she lied when she came aboard. She hid the fact that she was with child. If you are so concerned, go save the baby. If it lives, you will be charged with taking care of it, and that includes the indenture fee."

Tears ran down Matilda's cheeks as she returned to the hold. Even in the knowledge that it would cause her family great hardship, she was still willing to try to save the baby. But when she felt and listened to Katherine's belly, all was still. The baby was dead.

As Katherine's body was being lifted and carried to the porthole, Matilda requested that a prayer be said. Johann obliged her. It was a simple prayer: "Please, God, today accept into your kingdom Katherine Shaughnessy and her unborn baby. May they rest in peace."

Katherine and her baby would not be the last to be delivered into the depths of the ocean. All wondered who would be next.

The Kesslers thought their situation must be as bad as it could get, but they were wrong. Things got worse, a lot worse . . .

CHAPTER 10

THE STORM

After Katherine died, Matilda was not the same. Ulrich and Hannah constantly tried to do or say something that would make her smile, but nothing seemed to help. Hannah tried to get her interested in the needlework she'd brought aboard to help pass the time; she showed no interest. She was changing. Her smile was gone, and when she wasn't sleeping, as she often was, she sat staring off for long periods without moving. Her heart was broken, and she had lost all spirit and desire to go on.

Johann had no suggestions. He could only say, "It will pass." But his face began to look drawn and his wrinkles deepened, especially around his jaw. He constantly worried about his family. He was uncomfortably aware that the children had become painfully thin. Ulrich's clothing told the tale: he could hardly keep his pants up, and his shirts hung on him. But for now, Johann was most worried about Matilda.

The last week of the voyage changed their lives forever. A terrible storm came, with swells hitting the ship, causing it to sway back and forth. That day, Johann's family was eating their first hot meal in some time: hardly enough for one person, much less four, but at least it was something and it was warm. During the meal, a huge wave hit the vessel and everything went flying through the air. Passengers grabbed at anything to keep from being thrown across the hold; at least the cots were anchored to the wall and provided something stationary to hold. Johann caught hold of Hannah with one hand and the cot with the other. Ulrich seized a rail, which he felt cutting into his hand.

Eventually, Ulrich could hold on no longer. The next large wave broke his grip, and he was hurled through the air. He ended up lying facedown on the floor, pressed against a wooden barrel where tools were stored.

Neither of them had been able to help Matilda. She'd been thrown all the way across the hold and was hurt badly, bleeding from her forehead and the inside of her left forearm, which had a bone-deep gash. Johann carried her to the bed and was trying to stop the bleeding when the ship was hit by another swell. Ulrich and Hannah held onto the cot, and Johann braced himself against it, holding on to Matilda. Food, bedclothing, and waste from the toilet pots and anything else that wasn't tied down were again thrown all over the hold.

And then, as suddenly as they had come, the winds died down and the ship leveled. The passengers could still hear rain beating down on the deck of the ship, but they were grateful the wind had stopped.

Johann was able to stop the bleeding from Matilda's arm; he had taken off his shirt and torn it into strips to be used as bandages. It would suffice, he thought, until he could get help from the infirmary.

Then the ship started rocking again, not violently as before but just in a continuous up and down motion . . . up and down, up and down . . . continuously rocking as the rains pounded the deck. Water started seeping in. The men were placing pots under the leaks, but the pots slid every time the ship shifted, and more water came in. The cots were getting wet, and people were getting sick from the swaying. Many were still suffering from dysentery and were now lying in wet beds covered with vomit, feces, and urine. Some had chills, including Matilda. The family took turns trying to keep her warm and keep her wounds as clean and dry as possible.

The storm lasted for two and a half days, with wind and rain that would not quit. By the time it subsided, a large bump had appeared on Matilda's head, and the cut on her arm had become bright red and oozed a yellowish pus. Mostly she slept, but when awake she experienced lightheadedness and confusion. Her breathing was labored as if she were out of breath, even though she had hardly moved for several days.

Johann sought out Red Jack to ask if Matilda could be taken to the infirmary. But, as he had with Katherine Shaughnessy, Jack refused.

"We do not have the facilities to care for every passenger who gets a little sick," he said. "You knew the voyage would be difficult and that some would not make it. Your wife may be one of them."

Johann pleaded with him and offered more services at the end of the journey in exchange for help. Jack walked away, laughing.

"You have nothing to offer me," he said as he went. "Take care of your own problems."

A crew member who had overheard the conversation handed Johann a small container and told him to apply the contents to his wife's arm. Johann did so, and the solution was soothing but did little to help with healing. Nothing seemed to help. Many other passengers were sick and in need, but the crew offered no help, and more died. One man who died had so many lice on him that no one would touch him. Finally, a passenger asked a crew member for a tarpaulin or canvas they could use to carry him to the porthole and dispose of his body. This request, at least, was granted.

The passengers were told that they would soon be in America, if they could only manage to persevere.

All this time, Johann, Hannah, and Ulrich rarely left Matilda's side. They prayed, "Dear God, we ask that you send your healing grace upon our wife and mother. She is a good woman who has always tried to do your will. Amen."

There were moments when Matilda was lucid. She would tell them to be strong and make a great life in America. They kept telling her that they were almost there and that upon arriving they could get a doctor to make her well, but she continued to instruct them as though she knew she would not be with them. She made Johann promise that he would put in a big garden; she named all the vegetables and flowers she wanted him to plant there.

She also gave advice to Ulrich. "It is important to learn the language. Study the book. Help your father and watch after Hannah."

She told the children how much she loved them and that she was so proud to be their mother. They cried and begged her to hold on.

"In just days we will be in America, Mama," they said.

But their words of hope failed. She stopped speaking, and the next day as the family sat with her, there was a sudden stillness in the air, no breath from her body. They could see their mother and wife leaving. Then Johann hugged his children.

"Mama is gone," he said, his eyes blurring with tears. "She has left us."

As they all clung together crying, Johann said a prayer and kissed Matilda for the last time. Then the men came. Johann, Hannah, and Ulrich followed and watched as Matilda was carried and placed through the porthole, where she disappeared into the cold, dark water, her final resting place. The poem she had written as a child was still tucked inside her pocket, never to be read by anyone again.

During his last days on the *Webb*, Ulrich decided he would make a private tribute to his mother. Finding an old rusty nail, he carved her name and her birth and death dates into the floor of the ship, where they would be noticed by all the poor souls who would follow on this wretched vessel. He spoke to no one about this; it was his private tribute.

The last words he carved were "To my loving mother."

CHAPTER 11

MAMA REMEMBERED

For days after Matilda died, the family seldom spoke. Johann seemed to be in a stupor, unable to communicate or stay awake. Hannah's eyes were red and almost swollen shut from crying so much. Ulrich tried to comfort her, but his tears would always erupt, making each feel the loss even more.

It was on one of the rare days when they were able to go above for fresh air that they started sharing all the good memories they had of Matilda. They began by noting the physical characteristics the children had inherited from her: both were fairly tall like their father, while Matilda had been small in stature, but both had their mother's red hair and gray-blue eyes.

Then they started sharing stories about Matilda. Hannah and Ulrich both especially liked the story of how she had met their father, a story Matilda had never tired of telling. She had just turned sixteen when her father hired Johann to help with the large garden and make needed repairs around the property. Johann's full-time job was on a nearby dairy farm, but he would come on his day off throughout the summer to help with these chores.

Hannah and Ulrich laughed when they remembered how Mama had described Papa. She would say he was the tallest and skinniest person she had ever met. Johann would always laugh and say, "I'm still tall, but due to your mother's cooking, I'm no longer skinny."

Matilda had always said she was not very impressed with Johann when they first met. However, after a time, she saw qualities in him that she admired. She liked his honesty and how he always did a little extra for her father; she liked his strong blue eyes that did not look away when he talked to her. He was a polite and unassuming man who always showed her respect. He was fun to be with and often made her laugh.

Unfortunately, summer ended, and Matilda's father informed Johann that he would no longer need his help. Johann made a bold move and asked if he could visit Matilda on his day off. Her father agreed, and so the courtship continued. Not long after, Matilda's father became ill and never recovered, dying in just a few weeks, leaving Matilda and her mother alone. When Johann asked her to marry him soon after, she remembered how her father had spoken of Johann.

"He is a young man of good character and a friendly disposition," her father had said. "He is a man of whom almost all will take notice, with many capabilities to do things and do them well."

Shortly afterward, Johann and Matilda married.

At this point in the story, Matilda would always exclaim, "And before long, two of the most beautiful and smart gifts arrived on our doorstep!" She meant Hannah and Ulrich, of course. Remembering this brought smiles to Ulrich's and Hannah's faces. The real truth was that Matilda had been the gift to them, a special person who had the abilities to share her fondest memories while making new memories with the children. They had been blessed; how would they go on without her?

But soon they were telling more stories, still laughing, and their spirits lifted. After all, they still had these happy memories of Matilda; nothing could ever take those away. Ulrich noticed how Hannah changed as they talked; it was remarkable how much the laughter, fresh air, and sunshine brought the light back into her face.

However, it was not to last. Too soon, the crew was giving orders to go below. As they slowly joined the other passengers, Hannah and Ulrich both agreed they would help their Papa, all working together for the rest of the voyage. It was what their Mama would have wanted.

Ulrich silently wondered, though, whether they could survive the last few days living on this moving hellhole called the *Webb*.

CHAPTER 12

RED JACK OVERBOARD

Red Jack could perhaps have saved Matilda, but he hadn't. Ulrich hated him for that and wished for every horrible thing that one could imagine to happen to him.

Even after Matilda's death, Jack had no pity for the Kesslers. One day when Ulrich was carrying the last of a pot of hot water from the cookshop, Jack arrived with his kettle and instructed Ulrich to pour his own water into it; actually, as always, he shouted the instructions. Ulrich, trembling with fear, accidentally spilled some of the hot water on Jack's hand as he poured. Instantly, Ulrich felt the back of Jack's hand across his face, knocking him to the ground.

Johann had witnessed the incident. He turned toward Red Jack with both fists ready.

"What do you think you are doing?" he demanded.

Red Jack responded by hitting Johann across the face with the kettle, knocking him to his knees, blood pouring out of a gash under his right eye.

Then Jack, standing over Johann, said "So you want some water, eh?" and poured the rest of the hot water onto Johann's face.

His face burning with pain, Johann's first reaction was to fight back. He was a strong man and could easily have taken Jack. But Johann was also a sensible man, and he knew that attacking a crew member was a serious offense. If he did so, he would be put into the hole, a space about six feet by six feet, with only a piss pot and a small portal for light. Johann knew what the solitude of the hole could do to a person, robbing him of his dignity, his health, his very existence. Many died in there, and those who made it out were never the same, moving about like shadows.

Worst of all, if he were put into the hole, there would be no one to watch over his children—no one to protect them from people like Red Jack.

Johann silently rose, helped Ulrich up from the floor, and walked away.

As it turned out, soon no one would need protection from Red Jack. When they were only a few days out from the shoreline of America, Johann and Ulrich were asked by two crew members to come up to the top deck to help bring down the one remaining water barrel. As they were rolling the barrel toward the hatch, the ship was hit by a large wave. Johann and Ulrich both hit the deck hard. As they looked up, they saw Red Jack lurching toward them. Everything that was not bolted down was moving across the deck, including the water barrel. As they watched, the barrel hit Jack, throwing him down. He began sliding toward the left side of the ship, flailing like a fish out of water, one hand catching a buoy rope as he was going overboard. He was screaming for help as he tried to pull himself back onto the ship.

Johann hesitated, deciding whether to help him. Images of Matilda flashed in his mind. This man had let her die. Johann started to walk away but, in the end, could not. He tried to reach Jack, but another wave hit the ship, throwing Johann to the deck. In a matter of seconds, he was up again, but it was too late. Johann could no longer hear Red Jack, and all he saw was the buoy rope blowing about.

Red Jack was no longer. He had slipped into the same depths of the black sea into which he had watched, without feeling or remorse, so many passengers disappear.

Johann immediately reported the incident to Captain Bradford, who questioned him on what had happened but showed no anger against him.

"Mr. Kessler," he said simply, "I'm sure you did all you could."

But Johann thought, *Maybe if I hadn't hesitated . . .*

No one cared about Red Jack; even the other crew members were glad he was gone. The Captain made no mention of him the next day, and soon it was as though he had never existed, except for when the crew speculated about his death. Some thought several men had overtaken him while he was making his rounds and had thrown him overboard. Only the captain, Johann, and Ulrich knew what had really happened.

In the final analysis, it didn't matter. He was gone, and life on the ship was better without him.

CHAPTER 13

ARRIVAL IN AMERICA

Seven weeks had passed since they had seen land. The passengers' excitement was overwhelming when it came into sight on July 29, 1746. There was cheering, hugging, and laughing that had not existed for weeks. Only 247 of the 381 who had embarked were still alive to see the shores of America.

Johann, Ulrich, and Hannah stared at the land as the ship got nearer. A sadness overcame them as they thought of Matilda and how they wished she had lived to see this moment. They hugged, and Johann told them, "It will be all right."

After they docked, they were told they could not yet leave the ship's hold. Soon, two days had passed. The passengers were suffering in the hold due to the intense July heat. What they were enduring was unbearable cruelty. There was bewilderment, disgust, and rage among them. Madness had even taken hold of many. Desperate and helpless, they had no choice but to wait.

On the third day, hope arrived for those who were not sick or dying. The healthy passengers would be given medical exams to determine whether they were fit enough to leave the ship. Those too sickly to stand never had that chance; many more died.

Johann, Hannah, and Ulrich all passed their exams and were now to meet Hans Steiner. They'd been told he was a prosperous landowner in the area. There was no better feeling than being off the ship that bore so many horrible memories, but as they waited on the dock, standing on the "auction blocks," Johann thought of Matilda and it saddened him to tears. Still, as they felt the sun on their faces and the gentle breeze engulfing their bodies, they felt hopeful. Ulrich hoped he would never have to leave this place called Philadelphia, his new home in America.

Soon, Mr. Steiner approached them and introduced himself. Since he spoke German, he and Johann could talk easily, but it soon became clear that things were not going as planned. He said his request had been only for a young, sturdy boy around age fourteen. He needed a farmhand, not a family of three.

Johann tried to explain that Mr. Harvey Suter had promised back in Rotterdam that the family would stay together. He went on to explain that his wife had died on the ship and it was important that the rest of his family stay together. Ulrich could see that Mr. Steiner was getting upset with his father.

"That's nonsense," Mr. Steiner said. "I have no use for another girl on my farm. I could take you and the boy, but not the girl; she would only be a burden. So if you want to come with the boy, you can, but the girl stays. My contract is with Captain Bradford. I know of no Harvey Suter."

Now Johann was pleading, willing to do anything to keep his family together.

"I will work harder than any two men," he said, "and my daughter will work right at my side, along with my son."

Steiner would not back down.

"I suggest you say your goodbyes now," he said.

Ulrich's heart was racing as Hannah clung to him, crying uncontrollably. His father had signed a contract. How could this be their fate? How could Ulrich survive without his family?

Johann's own words sealed Ulrich's fate.

"It is a hard decision, Ulrich," he said slowly, "but I must stay with your sister; she could not survive on her own. In a few years you will be a grown man, able to take care of yourself."

Then Johann took from his pocket a most prized possession, a knife from his own father's army days. It was a small knife, only about five inches long; the short blade had mostly been used for cutting rope. However, as Ulrich knew, many of the soldiers had carried these knives strapped around their calves, to be used as a last resort for escaping a captor or in hand-to-hand fighting. The knife had a sheath covering the blade and could be hidden in the pocket of his trousers.

"Put this in your pocket," Johann said. "Do not display it, but use it if need be to protect yourself."

Hannah kissed and hugged her brother, thanking him for protecting her against Red Jack, for she would have been one of his victims had Ulrich not watched over her. She and Johann would be going back to the ship, but Johann assured his son that someone would come for them too, that they would not be on the ship much longer.

"Stay strong, son," he said. "I will be close by and will find you. We will one day be back together."

But as Ulrich was walking away with Mr. Steiner, he heard his father murmur, "Ulrich, my son, I never meant it to be this way. Please forgive me."

Upon hearing these words, Ulrich felt a strong need to hug his father, perhaps for the last time. It was needed and wanted by both. And so he ran back to his father, put his arms around him and held him tight, not saying a word.

Walking away again with Mr. Steiner, Ulrich blew his nose and wiped away tears, promising himself that this day he would become a man, that there would be no more tears. At the time, he didn't realize the pain that had been etched on his heart, a pain so deep that he would not be able to tell his story for many years.

Ulrich could not fathom what his life would be like from then on, but this he knew for certain: He had just escaped hell. In the Lutheran church, the preacher had given many sermons about hell, and Ulrich knew it existed on the ship he had just left. As he continued to walk through the town, he noticed people talking and laughing; all seemed happy in this new place called Philadelphia. He had not seen so many happy people for a long time.

CHAPTER 14

A NEW LIFE IN AMERICA

As they walked away, Mr. Steiner told Ulrich, still in German, that supplies would be purchased before they made the trip back to the farm. Arriving at the store, Ulrich saw it was well stocked, and Mr. Steiner purchased many items, things that couldn't be provided by the farm: large bags of flour, buckets for milking the cows, a chain, shells, bullets, tools, nails, and several jugs of what Ulrich assumed was strong drink.

Eventually, all was loaded onto the wagon and Ulrich was told to climb into the back. Mr. Steiner handed him a bag that contained a tin canteen of water, an apple, some dried meat, and soft, fresh bread. Ulrich had not eaten for a couple of days, and he'd had only a small amount of water. He had not had fresh bread or fruit for weeks. Just looking at the food and water made his dry mouth come to life. He consumed everything from the sack and was full for the first time in days. He could feel his eyelids growing heavy. Before long, he fell into a deep sleep.

When he woke, day was just beginning to break. Looking around, he saw a house, two barns, and several small buildings. He was barely awake when Mr. Steiner instructed him to help unload their supplies. After they finished the chore, they walked toward the barn and climbed up a ladder inside. When they reached the top, Mr. Steiner opened the door to a small loft area. There was a pallet and blanket, no chair, no table. It was sparse but clean. It was open to the outside, but Mr. Steiner said it could be closed in bad weather by closing the hatch overhead. He went on to say that there was a bucket by the well that Ulrich could use for drinking and bathing.

After weeks on the ship, Ulrich felt these arrangements would be fine. No more putrid smell, foul water, death.

"In the summer months," Mr. Steiner said, "you will sleep here; during the winter months you will stay in a cabin with Dutch, the other farmhand who lives on the property. The cabin has a wooden floor and a working fireplace. Dutch will be responsible for feeding you and giving you your daily chores. When you finish one chore, report back to him for the next. You will be moving around the farm, but be sure you are close by when it's time for the evening milking. Sunday is a day of rest except for the milking, which you and Dutch will continue to do. That will be your only chore for that day."

They climbed down from the loft and approached the cabin. A man close to Johann's age appeared in the doorway, and Mr. Steiner introduced him to Ulrich. This was Dutch. He barely looked at Ulrich as Mr. Steiner explained who Ulrich was and what jobs he would have on the farm. Then Mr. Steiner left and Ulrich began his work for the day.

Later that evening, Dutch seemed surprised at how fast Ulrich was at milking, especially when Ulrich was on his second cow and Dutch was still on his first. Dutch even checked the bucket and the cows to make sure Ulrich was performing the task properly. Ulrich informed him that he had been helping his father milk cows on the dairy farm since age six. This was one chore he knew he could do well.

CHAPTER 15

CHORES AND RULES

Every morning, Dutch would come to fetch Ulrich. As they went about their chores, Dutch explained how the farm operated, speaking German; he did not speak English. He was not very talkative beyond the farm instructions, but he did provide information about the Steiner family. There were three daughters. Two were married; the elder, Paulina, lived in a home near the tobacco fields with her husband and sons, and the younger, Louisa, was married to the minister's son and lived in town near the church. The youngest, Nia, who was about fourteen, was still at home. Dutch said that Nia was sickly and that he rarely saw her.

Dutch added that he never interacted with the women and girls of the family, only with the men. Mr. Steiner had requested that the hired help refrain from talking to his wife or daughters.

"That is only proper," he had said.

Ulrich heeded this and never ventured near the house. On Sundays, though, when the family gathered at the main house, he could hear laughter and smell food being prepared. That was difficult for him. He missed his family, especially his mother. His mind would wander, and he would think about Hannah and Papa. Where were they? What was happening to them? Were they looking for him?

Because the only chore on Sunday was milking, Dutch would sometimes take Ulrich fishing, showing him the best fishing holes and where to find worms and other bait such as crickets, grasshoppers, and leeches. They would always catch plenty of fish, usually catfish but also bream and trout. They would build a fire and roast the fish on the spot; what they did not eat would be taken back for later.

Sundays were special for Ulrich. He was learning a lot about life in the woods. Dutch was teaching Ulrich everything he knew about how to survive in the woods. Ulrich thought about his parents and how proud they would be of his newfound skills.

One of the farmhands' important chores was during the growing season of tobacco. Several days a week, they would walk to the fields, making sure that hornworms, budworms, and any other insects or weeds were not damaging the plants. On one particular day, as they walked, Dutch explained the harvesting of tobacco.

"The plants have already flowered," he said. "We'll have to cut the flowers off and wait about three weeks to start cutting the stalks. Mr. Steiner will hire many men from town or from other farms to work the fields. We will work in the fields until time for the evening milking. We will do this each day until all the stalks are cut, stripped, dried, and placed into barrels. The days will be long and hard; sleep will come easy.

"One more thing," he added. "Do everything Mr. Steiner's son-in-law, Dolf Stangl, tells you to do. He is a difficult man; try to stay close to me when he is around, and *never* question his authority."

Ulrich had come to trust Dutch. Dutch treated and fed him well; Ulrich would have liked more food, but he was never really hungry, as he had been on the ship. He knew how real hunger felt, how it was to eat stale, rotten food. With Dutch, he had no complaints.

Day after day, they performed the same routine: milking before daylight, making repairs, checking tools and utensils and, during harvest season, gathering the crops. Every morning they would have breakfast with the other men, head to the fields to do whatever chores needed to be done, and end the day's work with the evening milking. After supper with the men, Dutch would go to his cabin and Ulrich to his loft.

One evening after the milking, Dutch informed Ulrich, "Tomorrow we will start harvesting the tobacco. Get a good night's sleep, for in the morning I will awaken you an hour earlier than usual. That way, we can do the milking and still get to the fields in time to start working the tobacco when the other men arrive."

That night Ulrich barely slept, wondering how they would harvest all those fields. The next morning, as they finished the milking, daylight was just starting to break through. They soon arrived at the field, where they joined ten other men and were given instructions on how to proceed with the harvesting. Some men would be stripping the stalks and cutting them while others would be gathering the cut tobacco and loading the wagons.

At noon, they were fed in the field. This was hard, hot, grueling work, and after the meal, most all of the men lay down for a nap to help get them through the day. Ulrich joined them, but even so, the next morning he had no memory of even climbing the ladder to the loft at bedtime.

For several weeks, the routine stayed the same. Most of the men hired were drifters, generally looking for one or two days' work and then moving on. They were rugged, hard men, and they intimidated Ulrich. He stayed close to Dutch.

Finally, fall was arriving, and it was time to place the dried leaves in barrels called hogsheads. These would be inspected and sold, then taken by boat or rolled overland to tobacco ships.

Ulrich would be glad when it was over. The harvesting of the tobacco fields had made him feel certain that when he became a free man, he wanted nothing to do with farming.

"I know it's hard the first year," Dutch said, "but without the tobacco and wheat crops, the farm would not survive."

On the last day of the tobacco harvest, Mr. Steiner and his son-in-law, Dolf, were paying the workers as the last of the hogsheads were filled. In English, Mr. Steiner was bragging to Dolf about the indenture contract he had made with Captain Bradford and how profitable it had turned out to be.

"I will have the boy until he is twenty-one," Steiner said. "I had put in an order for a boy of fourteen, but they had this one instead, a ten-year-old. I will have him for an extra four years at the same price."

Ulrich listened to the conversation and wondered whether he had misunderstood Mr. Steiner. However, soon he realized he knew what he had heard, and he was suddenly filled with rage and hate, not only toward Captain Bradford and Mr. Steiner but toward his father. Had Papa known of this arrangement? Everything on the dock had happened so quickly, and Ulrich, only ten years old, had had no idea of what being indentured really meant. Maybe Papa hadn't known. But maybe he had.

Ulrich knew there was nothing else his father could have done on that dock to keep them all safe and together. For certain, though, his world shifted that day as he considered all that had happened. He began to blame Johann for Matilda's death, for losing his sister, even for leaving Rotterdam in the first place.

But Ulrich could do nothing about any of it. His future would be right here for a very long time. No one, he decided, was coming for him. He resolved to move forward as best he could.

He also resolved that day that he would keep his knowledge of English words a secret. He might learn something helpful if Mr. Steiner kept thinking he couldn't understand English.

By now the weather was changing; Ulrich had already started closing the loft hatch to stay warm. He wondered when he would have to go and live with Dutch. He liked having his own space, where he kept the knife and the phrasebook, his most treasured possessions. On every wall of the loft he had scratched the English words that he had practiced. On these cold nights, with the hatch closed, he said them aloud.

CHAPTER 16

WINTER IN THE CABIN

For several years, Dutch had lived by himself in the thirteen-by-fourteen-foot cabin. Ulrich would now be staying with him until planting time, some four months away.

For sure, Ulrich was now ready. Fall had come in with an inescapable chill, making it nearly impossible to stay warm in the loft. The day he was told to get his pallet, he ran as fast as he could, gathered his belongings, and within minutes was at the cabin.

As he entered, he was suddenly hit by the smell of something cooking and by the heat of the fireplace; he could hardly wait until bedtime to sleep by that warm fire. While he had been in the cabin many times, this was the first time he had noticed that the deerskins that hung on the walls were actually covering two windows, keeping the warmth in and the cold out. Beside the table and one chair sat a tree stump. Dutch informed him it was a place to sit and eat at the table. Also next to the fire were more animal skins, to be used as blankets.

Early on, Ulrich realized that one way to stay warm was to make sure the fire was stoked and an extra log or two thrown on during the night. When it was time to get up, the fire was still burning and the cabin was toasty.

His main thought during those cold winter months was that he would stay in the cabin until the cold was gone. Living with Dutch, though, he realized there were many more skills he could learn from him. He learned how to snare and skin a rabbit in less than a minute, dress a deer, tan a hide, and help prepare and cook all the wild game they hunted. They never were hungry that winter. One of Dutch's favorite stews was hasenpfeffer, though it was made from a rabbit, not from a hare "as in the old country." Ulrich heard that phrase from Dutch a lot during the winter.

Dutch had come up with a way of keeping their food safe from field mice, who were always trying to make a home in the cabin. He made a large pouch out of deerskin, with a drawstring, and he kept all the food supplies in the pouch. He hung it on a peg at the top of the rafters, with porcupine needles studded all around the rope. Not even the smartest critters got to the food. He had outsmarted them all.

Besides leftover vegetables from the garden, the Steiner family provided pickled vegetables, dried fruit, and on special occasions, fruit pies. In turn, Dutch killed and dressed turkeys to give to them. Dutch told Ulrich that he should "always return kindness with kindness and do a little more."

During the long winter months, Dutch and Ulrich chopped wood, mended fences, and helped repair anything that needed fixing. Dutch made Ulrich a proper chair and his own wooden plate and bowl, cup and spoon. Ulrich beamed when he saw them. Dutch also made Ulrich a cap and coat from leftover animal skins, saying he was tired of watching Ulrich shiver in the snow. The hat had a foxtail Ulrich could wrap around his face when the wind was strong.

All that winter, Ulrich's stomach was full and he felt warm and safe, with a comfortable place to sleep. He had plenty of clothes to face the harsh winter. But he often thought of his sister and father, still longing for them.

Dutch and Ulrich's main responsibility that winter was taking care of the livestock, keeping them healthy and fed. The hounds would gather the cows for the morning and evening milking. One word from Dutch and they were off, returning with six cows in tow. Never once did Ulrich or Dutch have to go to the pastures and fetch the cows. The dogs were great trackers and would also stir up game for Dutch, who was skilled at shooting. One day while they were hunting, he taught Ulrich how to load and carry a rifle, promising him that he would soon get a chance to shoot, and soon Ulrich did. Dutch always kept his promises.

After the evening meal, the hounds would be fed; afterward, they could be heard under the floorboards, scooting on their bellies until they reached the warmth under the fireplace. Ulrich wondered aloud why the dogs couldn't sleep in the cabin.

"They are animals and don't belong in here," Dutch replied.

Ulrich knew better than to push it.

Before long, spring arrived, warming the ground, melting some of the snow. Some of the lower areas still had patches of snow; however, when the trees started to bud, it was time for spring planting. Dutch explained to Ulrich that they would soon be very busy with the farm chores of plowing and planting, that he would be needed around the farm in different capacities, and that he should return to the barn loft, where he would be more available for the chores that Mr. Steiner wanted him to perform. Ulrich really didn't want to go back to the barn; he loved living in the cabin. He felt safe there. Dutch promised him that he could return next winter after the harvesting.

"Sundays will still be our day to hunt and fish together," he said. "If you venture into the woods by yourself, make sure you take the dogs with you. They will alert you to danger and protect you if need be."

Ulrich thanked Dutch for all he had taught him and for feeding him so well. He didn't realize he was thanking him in English. Dutch wanted to know how he had learned the new language. Ulrich told him about his mother and the phrasebook and about why he'd decided to keep his knowledge of English a secret after overhearing the conversation about his indenture.

Laughing and shaking his head, Dutch said, "Next winter, you bring the book with you and teach me." Ulrich promised he would and returned to the loft happier than he had been in a long time.

CHAPTER 17

THE BEATING

Days, weeks, months passed. Not much had changed on the farm except that Ulrich was a year older. He had grown a little, but it was still often noted that he was "skinnier than a beanpole."

One evening after the tobacco plants had been put into the ground, Ulrich had just finished the milking when Mr. Steiner walked up and told him he would be spending a few days working for Dolf Stangl.

"You are to do as he tells you," he said, "just as if it were me or Dutch telling you."

Fearful of how Dutch had described Dolf, Ulrich was reluctant to go, but he had no choice.

The days working for Dolf were long and hard, much harder than the life he was used to. Sometimes Dolf would work Ulrich and the farm's two slave boys in the hot sun for hours without a break. Water would be brought twice a day to the field, and lunch also would be eaten there, usually only bread and an apple. It was not unusual to see the two black boys eating feed corn directly from the cob.

Ulrich was careful not to anger Dolf. He had heard stories of Dolf whipping other servants; Dolf had even once branded a man for running away. Desertion was not that unusual, especially under a cruel master, but it carried the most severe consequences, like branding and shackles, and men like Dolf seemed to enjoy imposing them. Dolf's favorite tool for punishment was a riding crop. On occasion, he would get drunk, go to the servants' sleeping quarters, and terrorize them with the crop.

Soon Ulrich had been working on Dolf's side of the farm for weeks, and he found his health failing. One evening he was violently ill with diarrhea and vomiting. He needed fresh air and did not want to disturb the two slave boys he was living with, so he decided to walk outside. He stopped at the well and filled a tin cup with water, then walked about a hundred yards from the sleeping quarters, something he was not supposed to do. He was just about to return when he saw Dolf heading toward him on a horse. He could tell Dolf was angry as he dismounted, struggling not to fall, drunk as usual.

Ulrich tried to explain, but there was no reasoning with Dolf, who berated him, saying he was a liar and a good-for-nothing deserter. The more Ulrich talked, the madder Dolf got, taking another swig of the clear liquor known as "shine" and telling Ulrich he was going to teach him a lesson he would never forget.

Dolf walked over to Ulrich, carrying his riding crop, and backhanded him across the face with his free hand. The slap landed across Ulrich's eye, closing it immediately as he fell to the ground. He lay there, pain shooting through his eye. He then felt a hard object in his pocket under him and realized it was the knife his father had given him to protect himself. But it was no use. Dolf reached down to grab the back of Ulrich's shirt, and the knife fell to the ground. Ulrich was defenseless. Dolf unleashed another blow, this time with the crop, across Ulrich's forehead.

"I'm going to teach you to have respect for your master!" he said.

Before Ulrich could react, Dolf pulled him toward a nearby tree, stripped him of his shirt, and used the shirt to tie his arms around the tree. Dolf then walked around behind Ulrich and brought the crop down across his back, again and again, each time breaking the skin. Ulrich begged him to stop, but the blows kept coming, sometimes missing his back and hitting his buttocks and legs. Dolf beat him for so long that afterward Ulrich didn't remember how many times he had been struck.

After a while, his body just gave out. He fainted and sagged, held upright only by the arms of his shirt around the tree.

Dolf went back to the cabin and told the boys to go and get Ulrich, reminding them that Ulrich's fate was what would happen to any deserters on the farm.

Wide-eyed and shaking, the boys walked to the woods, where they saw Ulrich tied to the tree with his britches down and bloodied all over.

CHAPTER 18

AFTER THE BEATING

When Ulrich woke, the two slave boys were carrying him back inside the cabin. The pain was unbearable. Carefully, they laid him down on his stomach. As he lay there, they explained that the wounds needed cleaning. The cleaning seemed to go on forever, and every time they touched Ulrich, the pain was excruciating. They meant well, and maybe they saved Ulrich's life, but they weren't skilled at what they were doing. Afterward, though, they applied salve to help with the healing process and the pain. The salve was soothing, and Ulrich started to feel better.

He wanted to sleep, but they told him he needed to stay awake. So he asked them where they were from and how they'd gotten to the Steiner farm. Even though the three of them had worked side by side during the past two weeks and had eaten and slept in the same cabin, they had never talked much to one another; that night he listened as they told their story.

They were brothers. They had arrived on the farm about two years earlier. Before that, all they had ever known was the farm they were born on. As they told the story, a great sadness came over them, especially when they described the day they were taken from their mother. Ulrich understood their pain, as he had also lost his family. They all had suffered.

As the story continued, it became apparent that Mr. Steiner was not happy that Dolf had purchased two slave boys. He didn't believe in slavery, only indenture. The boys relayed a story of how they heard Dolf explain to Mr. Steiner how owning slaves was more profitable than making indenture contracts. Dolf told Mr. Steiner that in time, he would come to agree. Mr. Steiner just shook his head and walked away.

The oldest boy explained that at first, life on Dolf's farm was not that bad. Dolf's wife Paulina, the "missus," was a kindly woman. During the growing season, each week a basket full of vegetables, eggs, and biscuits was left inside the cabin; in the winter there were dried beans, cured meat, and fresh eggs as well as extra blankets.

"We were living good compared to some," the older boy said, "even though we were missin' our mama."

As they continued their story, they told Ulrich it had all started to change when Dolf started drinking more and his true self surfaced. Both had experienced his wrath, but not to the extent of Ulrich's beating. Early on, they had learned to keep their distance and always to obey Dolf, never questioning his authority.

The boys continued to talk about Dolf and how mean he could be, especially when he was drinking. They began telling Ulrich a story about an old horse named Henry. It was a particularly sad story but so involving that it let Ulrich forget about his pain for a short while.

One day they were plowing a field with Henry, and suddenly

the horse just refused to move. Sometimes horses will do that as a message that they need rest, but Dolf didn't see it that way and began hitting Henry with the riding crop. Henry didn't move a bit, but Dolf kept hitting him. The horse was old, but that didn't matter to Dolf. After a while, Dolf walked a distance away and returned with a piece of fence board.

"He hit the poor hoss as hard as he could with that board," said the older boy. "Old Henry's front legs buckled and he went down on his haunches. Master Dolf hit him again and again. He's a mean man when he gets mad, and he was powerful mad that day. We were sad for Henry, but we were more scared of Dolf. Finally, Henry just rolled over on his side and died. Dolf cussed and kicked him and told him, 'Get up, you no-good bastard.' But soon he realized that Henry was dead. He told us to go to the barn and get two shovels and bury Henry right where he lay, right there in the field. He told us if we told anybody what had happened, we would get some of the same. We did exactly what he told us. It took all the rest of the day and into the evening hours, but we got it done."

It seemed that from that day on, Dolf had only gotten meaner. Every animal on the farm had been mistreated by him in some way.

"Don't rightly know what makes a man so mean," the older boy continued. "Most critters will obey you with just a little push. No need to beat them. But Master Dolf always carries that crop around. Seems like he's just waiting to hurt something when he can. Can't say for sure whether he's ever mistreated the missus or their boys. He's probably too afraid of Mr. Steiner to do that."

As the boys continued to talk, Ulrich found himself needing sleep.

It soon took over, and he slept until the next morning, waking up in severe pain. Instantly, he was reminded of what had happened the night before. He was completely drained of all will to stand, even though he tried to do so. Suddenly, he felt hands helping him to right himself. It was the two slave boys, with an explanation.

"We did your chores this morning so you can rest," the younger boy said. "And we have some food for you when you get hungry. Master Dolf and his missus and young 'uns will be gone all day. He told us you are going back to Master Steiner's farm tomorrow."

Tomorrow couldn't come soon enough for Ulrich. He thanked the boys and let them know that he would pass their stories on to Dutch. They both asked him not to, in fear that Dolf would take it out on them if he heard back that they were telling stories. Old Henry was still vivid in their minds. Ulrich told them that he would only tell Dutch and that Dutch was a man who could be trusted.

They said they hadn't come to know any men like that.

CHAPTER 19

DUTCH TELLS HIS STORY

Ulrich returned to the farm early Monday morning before daylight and went straight to the loft. Later that morning, Dutch came to get him for the morning milking. Upon seeing Ulrich, he realized Ulrich had been beaten terribly: one of Ulrich's eyes was completely swollen shut, a large welt crossed his forehead, and when he tried to stand and walk, his gait was uneasy.

Ulrich saw an anger in Dutch's face that he had never seen before. Dutch's neck and lower jaw looked swollen, with veins popping out.

Dutch asked one question: "Did Dolf do this?"

Ulrich nodded.

"Stay in bed today," said Dutch. "I will do your chores."

That evening, Dutch came to take Ulrich to the cabin. He had prepared a meal there. As Ulrich was eating, he began talking to Dutch, explaining how some men want to break others like they break horses and that Dolf was one of those men.

"I know Dolf hurt you physically," he said. "That will heal in time. Do not let him hurt your spirit. And I have spoken to Mr. Steiner. He has seen the cruelty in his son-in-law and has already told him his punishments are too harsh. He will not let this kind of treatment go on. Now take off your shirt and britches so I can see what he did."

Dutch might have killed Dolf that night, had he had a chance. Just looking at the damage brought tears to his eyes. Large welts solidly covered Ulrich's back, buttocks, and legs, down to his ankles. Dutch could tell that Dolf had used the crop, his favorite item to inflict pain.

Dutch cleaned the wounds and applied salve to each welt. That night Ulrich stayed in the cabin, and it was Dutch's turn to tell his life story, thinking that perhaps hearing it would ease Ulrich's pain and help release some of the anger Ulrich was feeling. In many ways, their stories shared some of the same events.

And so he began.

"I was a young boy from a small German village. My father was a cheesemaker on a modest farm, with a small but comfortable home for me and my sister, who was five years older. My parents were not young when she was born, and when I came along, it was a complete surprise. My mother's health never returned after I was born, and she died when I was eleven. My father grieved, and I felt that he always blamed me and my sister to some degree. My sister married at sixteen, probably to get away from all the sadness in our home. The farm and the cheese business deteriorated. I did what I could to hold things together, but it was not enough. Father had given up, and he died four years later.

"I went to live with my sister and her husband on their farm. I worked for my brother-in-law but saw no future for myself. I found my escape when I heard about getting free passage to America as an indentured servant for a few years. A new land with a future. I said my farewells and boarded the ship. I was eighteen, strong and healthy, excited about my new adventure. I kept mainly to myself on the ship, sleeping as much as possible so I could keep up my strength. I rationed my food as long as I could. It was a dreadful and disgusting place for any human to have to endure for a day, not to mention weeks. Many gave in to the misery and died."

Ulrich's mind started to drift back to the horror that he had experienced on his voyage. Dutch could see that he was getting through to the boy, so he continued the story.

"After about six weeks, we landed in America. I was quickly released to a farmer, a Mr. Alfred Schnurr, who grew tobacco, corn, and wheat. That is where I learned to farm crops; I had grown up on a dairy farm, and that was all I knew. Mr. Schnurr was a wealthy farmer and had several indentured servants, five men and three women. It was a large farm, and we all struggled to stay healthy because the living conditions were not good. We were each given one blanket, a wooden plate, a spoon, and a tin cup. Our beds were often made of hay—that is, until it was needed for the animals. In the summer, we worked ten or more hours a day at plowing, planting, weeding, and harvesting, plus any other chores deemed necessary by the overseer. In the fall, all hands were needed to harvest the crops, especially the tobacco. Even the women would sometimes be called to the fields for tobacco stripping, though mainly they were used for domestic chores: washing, cooking, gardening, and preserving food.

"There was a girl named Helena, also indentured, whom I took a liking to. Every day as she dished out the food, I could tell her eyes lingered on me a little longer than on the others. One day, I tripped over myself as I was looking her way, and she smiled at me and said, 'Be careful.' That made me feel she also felt something for me, and it turned out she did.

"Before long, Helena and I started meeting in the dark of night or at any spare moment during the day. During rainy days and harsh winter days, when there was less work to do, we would meet and talk and dream about what we would do when we were no longer indentured, when we were free. Each day became a dream of excitement because we now had hope of a future. The prospect of being able to marry and have our own land filled us with joy.

"But all this soon changed. My father had a saying, *Whatever will be, will be*, and indeed, life can be altered quickly, as mine was. One night, early in October, everything changed drastically, and there was nothing I could say or do to prevent it. I now understood what my father had meant.

"It was a Saturday night, and we were all getting ready for bed when we heard men shouting and a lot of movement and chaos. I saw men moving toward me, and suddenly I found myself in a wagon with all my meager belongings and with two other indentured men, Terrance and Alphonse. One of the other men guarded us with a gun. Within minutes, the wagon was rolling; to where, we had no idea.

"'Don't think about running,' the guard said. 'You won't get far.' He was a mean-looking character with a full beard and a large scar that ran below his cheekbone almost to his upper lip, and he grinned as he rubbed the barrel of the rifle like someone petting a dog.

"The air was cold; we were all shivering as we continued the journey through the night. After several hours, we came to the end of the road, and to my right I could see a barn. We were told by the guard to get out of the wagon and go into that barn. He shouted at us to move quickly. I thought of running, but I knew I would probably be killed or, even worse, captured and brought back.

"As we entered the barn, I could see four horses in stalls. We were instructed to sit against one of the walls while the men tied our hands behind our backs. Terrance balked at this and was hit in the face with the butt of the rifle and told to shut his mouth. Soon we were all secured and left there without further word. Alone, we started talking about why we were there. Where was Mr. Schnurr?

"Terrance said, 'I have heard of people being traded for various reasons, one being gambling debts and no other way of paying them. Mr. Schnurr must have done that with us. Otherwise he would never have let this happen; he was very protective of his property.' I didn't want to believe this, even though it seemed logical.

"Soon sleep came over the three of us until we were awakened by the Dog, the name we had given the guard because when he talked it sounded like a growl and because he was dirty and stank of tobacco juice. He reminded us of a vicious watchdog, one we would not want to make mad.

"As we left the barn, I now saw the encampment and other men moving about. We walked over to a three-walled structure with an overhang and a fire pit surrounded by stacks of wood and crude, lean-to shelters. We were told that this was where we would eat, sleep, and live when not working.

"Another man approached and asked us if we spoke German. We all said *ja*. He then explained that he was the road gang chief and that we were there to help build the road. We would be removing trees, stumps, brush, boulders, and anything else in the way of the surveyor. He said, 'You will be given a biscuit and coffee in the morning, and the chow wagon will bring lunch to you in the field. You will be given the evening meal upon returning to the campsite. Go now and get your coffee and biscuit. You start work today.'

"We could see the Dog on his horse in the background, with rifle in hand."

CHAPTER 20

THE CAMP

"And so began my life as a road builder. Before anything could be done each day, the surveyor would determine distance, direction, and elevation. Distance was measured by an iron chain sixty-six feet long. It was known as a surveyor's or Gunter's chain. Each link in the chain measured 7.92 inches long. The chains were stretched out completely and marked with a pole. This process continued until 88 chains were laid down; that measured one mile.

"Mile after mile was done the exact same way. It was important that the elevation done by the surveyor was correct, because a wagon could only traverse a vertical rise of 462 feet per mile.

"For several weeks, Terrance, Alphonse, and I cleared, flattened, and graded as the chain was moved. It was backbreaking labor, supplied mainly by indentured men. Every day we were issued tools, hoes, steel wedges, and shovels for dislodging large rocks which we then hauled away. Some men who were known and trusted by the bosses were issued axes and machetes for clearing trees and brush.

"It was hot and humid outside, with mosquitoes and other insects.

Maybe the worst of all were the black flies. We had no protection other than completely covering our bodies with the foul mud of the swamp that surrounded the road. We also had to watch for moccasins and other snakes. One man fell down an embankment into a nest of copperheads, and when we found him, he was swollen so badly that he was unrecognizable. Often, horses would be brought to help remove large stumps that the men could not get out by hand, and one man was dragged to death by a horse that was spooked by a loud noise made by a breaking chain.

"The encampment had about thirty men. All were indentured. Ten were indentured convicts who had come to America to earn their freedom rather than serving prison sentences. The rest were simple indentured men, either bought by the road company or sold to it by cruel men such as the Dog. All were just looking for a better life.

"The encampment had strict laws: no fighting, no stealing, and especially no trying to escape or even wandering out of the camp. Anyone breaking the laws was severely punished: they were beaten, denied rations, or worst of all, had their terms of service extended. So most obeyed out of fear. We three mainly stayed to ourselves, as we'd been told by others that groups of men looking out for one another would benefit all.

"The first winter turned out to be milder than most, and my companions and I were grateful for that. And we had enough to eat, thanks to the cook, who had creative ways to keep us from starving, though we were always on the edge of hunger. The surveyor, who was a decent man, brought in canvas that could be nailed to the sides of our lean-tos; when it was cold or rainy, we could bring the two pieces of canvas together to give us protection. He also gave us extra water breaks so we could rest, if only for a few minutes. The overseers, whom the men called bullmastiffs, never questioned his authority. He was the only person who knew how to survey; he was in charge. He even encouraged the cook to play his fiddle at night after chow. Some of the men would join in with song. At times, the encampment was almost bearable . . .

"My spare time was spent marking off the days and months until I would be free. I could only hope that Helena would wait for me. Had I known what I know now, I might have jumped from the wagon that first night and taken my chances . . . but I didn't.

"Soon I had just one more year to serve. Other men came in that summer, and some, who had earned their freedom, left. By luck or chance, one day the surveyor told me I'd be helping to move the chains and poles, a much easier job. It was a welcome relief for my body for several months. That ended all too soon, when the man who had done that job returned; still, I was grateful for having had that time.

"I became more and more anxious as I came near the end of my time. As fate would have it, that last winter was extremely harsh. Despite the cook's best efforts, food was scarcer than before. Supplies arrived only once a month, and there was never enough. Hunger for some was so bad, they would boil water in their tin cups and put in handfuls of termites, ants, or other insects to eat. It was so cold, we wrapped our hands in rags or anything we could find to prevent frostbite. Men broke down and wept; some just lay down and died. And among those who were still alive, there was much fighting.

"I started thinking about what I could learn that might help me once

I was free. We were sometimes able to hunt down deer and rabbits, which provided most of the food we did get during that last winter, and I volunteered to help the cook gut the animals. My theory was to learn as much as possible about how to survive in the wilderness. The cook also gave me a deer hide and showed me how to tan it. At night, I would knead the hide to soften it, in hopes that items could be made from it that would be useful to me and my companions.

"Cook knew how to forage for nuts, berries, mushrooms, even chicory, to supplement our diet. He knew a lot about healing too, and he would scavenge for herbs that could heal wounds and bring down fevers. For sure, many would not have survived without his help, not just physically but because of those few minutes around the evening campfire when we could escape the monotony of our lives by singing along to his fiddle music.

"Every man in the camp came to depend on the cook for so many things. We all just called him Cook; I never knew his name. One night, he shared with me his own story, and now I will tell it to you exactly as he told it to me."

CHAPTER 21

THE COOK'S STORY

"Dutch, you are not going to believe what I am about to tell you. It's a miracle I am here to tell you at all. This is my story, the way it was told to me many times, by many different people.

"It seems there was a group of Shawnee women foraging in the woods for a certain root. It was one of the older women who first heard a sound. A few more minutes passed, and she heard it again; it was familiar, but she couldn't hardly make it out. She thought it could be an animal in pain.

"As she got closer to the large oak tree, though, there was no doubt about it; the sound was a baby whimpering and crying. 'How could this be?' she called out to the others.

"As they came closer, each woman froze in place after hearing the sounds. They spotted a fresh mound of dirt. A stone with some kind of marking was placed on top of the mound. They frantically started digging the dirt; as they did, the cries became stronger. Beneath, they found a small wooden box, tied with rope. They cut the rope and opened the box, and that is when they found me: a white baby boy, wrapped in a blanket, barely alive.

"The woman who had first heard my cries, Odina, took me from the box and told the others, 'He will not survive much longer without milk; take him to Koko and have her feed him.'

"Koko had just had her own baby boy and could give me what I needed, a mother's milk. She did, and I survived. Koko treated me as her own and in time named me Ahanu. I guess I was a pretty happy baby, because that name means 'he laughs.'

"My childhood was filled with many happy days. My brother Huritt and I were inseparable; we did everything together. There were no more children, so we got all the attention.

"Eventually, I realized I looked different than the others and questioned my mother. She told me how I had come into her life and how she had adopted me and loved me as her own.

"It was assumed that my birth mother thought I had died. She gave me a proper burial but then had to move on. It was just luck and the Great Spirit that brought the women to rescue me. I would not have survived the night.

"Over the years, I came into contact with others like me, and I realized I wanted to know more of the white man's world. Hearing their strange languages and seeing how I looked like them pulled me in that direction. French trappers came often to trade, and when they did, I listened. In time, I learned a few French words.

"I had just turned eighteen when a group of trappers came to our village looking for someone who was interested in being a guide. I was more than interested and agreed to guide them for a month; as it turned out, I stayed with them almost a year.

"By then, I was eager to return to my tribe and my family. However, upon arriving, I found they were no longer there. They had been driven out by the Iroquois. I was told they were headed to Pennsylvania; they spoke the same language as the Lenape and Delaware, tribes native to that area.

"The next day, I started my journey to find them. I lived with the Delaware for a time, continuously searching for my people. After the year, I gave up. To this day, I have not found them.

"I then decided to travel to the city of Philadelphia. I bartered for white man's clothing and was accepted as a young Frenchman.

"The first year was difficult. I washed dishes, cleaned out stalls, swept the streets. I did any work I could find. Along the way, I learned a few German and English words along with my French. This helped me acquire a job with the local butcher. He was a German man and needed someone to make deliveries.

"On one of those deliveries, I met Alena. She worked for a family as one of the cooks, and she was the one who always accepted the packages I delivered to their kitchen. She was beautiful, and seeing her was the one thing I looked forward to each week.

"Soon we became friendly, talking together each week. Finally, I became bold enough to ask her if I could come by and see her on her day off. She said yes, and so our courtship began.

"One day the butcher was struggling, trying to show an apprentice how to cut into bone. Boldly, I asked if I could show him. After that day, I became the new apprentice; a few months later, Alena and I married.

"We were very happy and all was going well, except for one thing. Alena had three miscarriages in two years. She desperately wanted children, but it seemed it was not to be. After ten years and several more miscarriages, we gave up hope. We were happy with each other, and that would have to be enough. It was a great surprise when we discovered she was with child once again. This time, she was able to carry the baby, and many months passed without a problem. But when the baby finally came, she was stillborn. Alena died a few weeks later from complications of the birth. I was brokenhearted, moving through my days in a fog. Only my work at the shop kept me going.

"Then, one day, a man walked into the shop asking if we knew of a cook who would be willing to live with and cook for men building a road. Later that day, I contacted him. I wanted to get away from the city and all the things that that reminded me of Alena. I wanted to return to the land. I have been working for him for the past five years.

"One more thing: I found out that the markings on the stone at my infant gravesite were of a Gaelic cross. So I might be Irish.

"So here we are, my friend, each in our own way, trying to survive."

CHAPTER 22

DUTCH MEETS MR. STEINER

Here Dutch paused for a moment, remembering. Finally, he spoke again.

"When I left camp, Cook was the only person I truly missed. I will be forever grateful for all he taught me. It was a blessing to have such a man in my life.

"Cook did not tell me his story because he wanted sympathy but because he knew the hardships I had been through. He was telling me as a source of encouragement. All have struggled, Ulrich; some more than others, but all have had hardships. The cook survived his, I survived mine, you will survive yours.

"That winter in the road camp, we all heard the same rumor that no more land or tools were being given to freed indentured servants. At best, we might get new clothing, a horse, some food, and a small amount of money. I did not know what to expect.

"Finally, the day of my departure came. I handed over the tanned skins to Terrance and Alphonse, who each had six more months, and told them to see Cook. He would know what to do with the hides. We shook hands and vowed to reunite after their time was up, but that never happened.

"In the barn where the horses were kept lay my new clothes, a sack of dried meat and hardtack, and a document saying I had finished my time and was a free man. I was twenty-two. Outside, my horse awaited; he was old and swaybacked. I only hoped he could make it back to the farm.

"Now I will finish the story. I am sorry: I have talked longer than I should have."

But Ulrich liked the story and asked to hear more. Dutch handed him an apple and a biscuit and continued on.

"I headed back down the road we had come in on. It took five days to make the trip on the old horse. His name was Gersund. The name had been given to him as a joke, since as you know, it is the German word for "healthy." He wasn't a healthy horse, but he got me to my destination. I decided to stop outside the farm and rest Gersund. I would wait until milking time to go in and surprise Helena.

"It never happened. I was the one surprised, because I was told Helena had been sold shortly after I'd left. No one knew where she had gone. Mr. Schnurr had become a drunk, spending his days drinking and gambling, trading many of his indentured servants for his debts. The farm was barely functioning, with only two servants left; they were actually free, having served out their indentures, but they were older and had nowhere else to go.

"So began my days of wandering, working odd jobs for food or a place to sleep while searching for Helena. I asked everyone I came into contact with, but no one had knowledge of her."

Dutch paused for a long moment before he continued.

"Soon I became exhausted, needing to find work that would pay more than food and a place to sleep. Mostly I slept in the woods, in fact, until the day I saw Mr. Steiner. He was hiring extra help to work on his farm temporarily. He was offering two meals a day and a place to sleep, along with pay. That was good enough for me.

"Every day I worked the tobacco fields. I had worked on tobacco and other crops while working for Old Man Schnurr, so I knew what I was doing. After one long and hard day, Mr. Steiner requested to speak to me, asking where I had lived and what I had done in the past. I explained how I had come to America from a small village in Germania. He was surprised, because his family had migrated from the same area when he was five years old. Evidently, he felt a bond.

"'I am impressed by your knowledge of tobacco,' he said. 'Two of my best men just got up and left one day without any notice. I am in need of an extra hand permanently. Would you be interested?'

"A chance to stay in one place, with no more wandering: this was more than I had ever expected. Suddenly, I no longer felt alone and isolated. Before I even knew what the pay would be, I said yes. As we walked together, though, he did tell me about the pay and about the small cabin by the stream where the two hired men had lived. They had not made any repairs, and it was in need of work.

"As we came upon the cabin, I could see for myself that much work was needed. As we entered, I saw that several floorboards needed nailing down. The fireplace was full of ashes, and as I looked up, I could see the sky through a hole in the roof. In one corner was a table with two chairs—one of them broken—and a bed and a couple of iron pots. As bad as it looked, it was a whole lot better than sleeping in the woods. I told Mr. Steiner I would make all the repairs and even build a new front door with a large wooden latch. Each day I cut firewood, and I started planting the vegetable garden. I even built a chicken coop, and Mr. Steiner provided me with a few hens.

"One of the best days was the day he showed up carrying a rifle and two black and tan hound pups.

"'With the rifle,' he said, 'you will be able to hunt your meat for the winter. Deer, rabbit, turkey, and pheasant are plentiful in the area. With some training, these pups will be good hunting partners. They come from good stock. The rest of the litter went to my son-in-law.'

"I ate well that winter with what Mr. Steiner had supplied to me; it made me feel like a rich man. It has been a solitary life here, but like all men who are grateful, I count my blessings.

"I have to tell you, though, that when Mr. Steiner showed up that day with you, I was none too happy. Sharing my time, my space, was not something I was sure I wanted. However, after a while I could see that you needed some guidance and training, just like the pups, and now I am glad you came and that I am part of your life and you are part of mine.

"My hope in telling you my story is that it will help you heal inside your head. Your body will take a while, and you may always have those scars."

With that, Dutch ended his story. It had been a long day, and soon both Dutch and Ulrich drifted into a deep slumber.

CHAPTER 23

GOING TO TOWN

In time Ulrich's injuries healed, and only a couple of scars remained to remind him of the beating. Several months after Ulrich's return to the Steiner farm, Dutch told him that the two slave boys were no longer on Dolf's farm. They were now living on a farm in the area with other slaves, and while they were not free, he had been assured that at least they would not be mistreated there. Ulrich hoped he was right.

Mr. Steiner had been hearing more and more stories about his son-in-law's drinking and spending days away from his farm, and he had heard about the abuse. So he'd taken it upon himself to find a new place for the slave boys and to hire someone who could stand up to Dolf and keep watch over Paulina and her children. He'd thought of John Michael Lewis, a free man who worked on a nearby farm. John could speak both English and German and was known as an honest and kind man. Best of all, he was six feet four and very muscular, which had given him the nickname "Big John." Dolf would not be using his riding crop either on or around Big John.

Knowing all this, Ulrich had moved on from his terrible experience with Dolf, and when Mr. Steiner, Dutch, and Dolf went into Philadelphia to buy supplies, he was glad to go with them. These days were treasured experiences, giving Ulrich a glimpse of what life was like off the farm. While days on the farm were mainly the same, the time spent in town was exciting. He thought of himself as a great explorer on an adventure, each time learning something new.

Once a year, Dutch would take him to town to buy him new clothing. Much of his clothing was hand-me-downs, but on that special day, he would get new breeches, stockings, and shoes.

"Boy, you are growing too fast, making my purse lighter," Dutch would complain. Of course, all was said with a smile, and they would both laugh because they knew Ulrich was not going to stop growing. In fact, by the time he left the Steiner farm he would be three inches taller than Dutch and just as strong.

Sometimes, on these trips to town, Ulrich would almost forget his situation. Instead of being an indentured servant with a man who worked at the same farm, he imagined he was a son with his father, making purchases.

He especially enjoyed the meals they ate at the Tun Tavern on Front Street, close to Christ Church and the Quaker meeting house. There were many taverns in Philadelphia, City Tavern being the most popular. There was also the Man Full of Troubles and George Bows Out with a Blowout, but Dutch favored the Tun Tavern. When Ulrich asked him why they never ate at another tavern, Dutch simply replied it was because the Tun Tavern had the best food. He would say nothing more.

Later Ulrich learned that the other taverns, especially George Bows

Out With a Blowout, were used as meeting places where politics was discussed, often ending in a brawl. Perhaps Dutch did not want him to witness that. He also learned that while Philadelphia prided itself as a city of tolerance and diversity, many taverns excluded indentured servants. The Tun did not.

Ulrich did not really mind always eating at the Tun. Dutch was right that the food was delicious: big bowls of food piled high, two kinds of meat, including something delicious called a Red Hot Beef Steak, and pie with lots of coffee. Ulrich would eat until he thought he might explode. It was more food than they would have in three days back on the farm. But as much as he enjoyed the food, the smells of freshly baked pies, biscuits, and cornbread made him think of his mother and how much he missed her.

After their midmorning meal, he was given instructions which were always the same: "Do your exploring, stay out of trouble, and meet me back at the wagon to start loading this afternoon around three o'clock." And that is what he did. Like a wild animal being set free, he took in as much as possible in those few precious hours.

Down Water Street were many taverns, and Ulrich would watch the goings-on there. The Man Full of Trouble, for instance, was popular among shipwrights, dockhands, and cordwainers, who made shoes from new leather. Most of the taverns also rented rooms, and patronizing the Man Full of Trouble were sailors who dropped anchor for short stays in Philadelphia. Not overly endowed with money, the men would often share a bed with as many as three others, but it still was better than the ships they had just left.

Ulrich never went inside a tavern by himself, but he would go in and out of shops. He also often stopped to watch boys his age and older playing games. He later discovered that one game was called "jacks." Another, a game of counting, was played with dice. He was interested, but he never lingered long enough to ask if he could play. He decided there was too much to see to spend time playing games.

Philadelphia was a busy place; trade and commerce were booming. Ulrich longed for the day when he could leave the farm and be a part of city life. He loved the city and all of its lures, the busy people building and selling things. He especially liked to visit the new textile mills, which were just coming into their own. He didn't realize that what he was watching would play a big role in his future.

He also liked looking at the large mansions along the waterfront of the Delaware and Schuylkill Rivers. It was hard for him to believe that only one family occupied each house. The mansions symbolized power, and he never tired looking at them; the beauty and size overwhelmed him. He could walk for hours in awe of the magnificent structures.

Even though he much appreciated the beauty of the architecture, it saddened Ulrich to watch enslaved boys and girls working on the properties. Some of the boys were no older than he was when he had first arrived on Mr. Steiner's farm. He wondered whether these boys were also separated from their families. He asked Dutch about it one day.

Dutch laughed. "You are the most curious person I have ever known!" he said, not for the first time. But then he sobered as he explained.

"Ships, much like the ones you and I came to America on, brought the slaves from other countries to these lands. They were taken by force: men, women, and children. If they survived the trip—and many do not, as we both know—they would be sold to people who bid on them. As with you and me.

"But the slaves can never work their way to freedom. They are bred, like animals, to provide an endless labor force. The lucky ones get to work in the homes as servants instead of toiling in the fields under cruel overseers, but even in the house they are not safe from abuse, and many times the masters of the house have their way with the young girls.

"Some black folks that you see in town are slaves who were given their freedom. They are rare. Some escaped into freedom, but this is even more rare due to the punishment administered to slaves if they are caught. They can be whipped and even branded, and they are made to perform extra chores on less food.

"We both know how horrible the conditions on the ship were. Imagine all that and being shackled, having no knowledge of the language or where you are going or what your future holds."

What Dutch said made Ulrich sad. He realized that no matter how hard his life had been, he would be a free man someday. What would it be like to live without that hope?

Neither of them said a word for the rest of the trip. But that lesson, like so many Ulrich learned from Dutch, would stay with him for the rest of his life.

CHAPTER 24

ULRICH TURNS EIGHTEEN

Many changes occurred the year Ulrich turned eighteen.

He had acquired his own rifle and managed to bring down a couple of deer and some other game by himself. He still stayed with Dutch during the winter months and could only use the gun when hunting with him. Since the beating by Dolf, Ulrich and Dutch had grown closer, and they talked more together. Dutch once told Ulrich he was like a son to him. With Dutch's help, Ulrich had made it this far, becoming a man. Now his freedom was near.

He wasn't sure why, but he had never been sent to Dolf's side of the farm again. And while his physical scars had faded and he'd learned to be in Dolf's presence without feeling rage, he had vowed that no man would ever beat him again. He would die fighting first.

Dutch had always told him that in time something bad would happen to Dolf, and it did.

Dolf was killed in an accident. Dutch, Dolf, and Mr. Steiner's other son-in-law, Lenard, were cutting trees together and one fell, crushing and killing Dolf. Dutch and Ulrich helped Mr. Steiner and Lenard carry the coffin to the burial site. No tears were shed; even Paulina was stoic. Ulrich noticed that their children, too, seemed unmoved. They just stared straight ahead as if they were in a trance. He wondered whether it was because they were so young and didn't understand or whether they had been abused by their father.

As Ulrich walked back to the farm behind the family, his own memories of his night of horror with Dolf came back. The rest of the family returned to the farm. He returned to the loft.

Soon afterward, Dutch was told that Paulina would be moving back home with her two boys and that they would all start working on the farm. Ulrich would move into Dutch's cabin and live there year-round. Dutch would move into Dolf's former house and would be in charge of that side of the farm. After the move, Dutch became loved by all who worked there, for they had hated Dolf, whom they had called "the devil."

Another event that changed their lives was the day Mr. Steiner brought home Kathleen Doyle. She had been recommended by the doctor in town to help with Nia, who was growing more and more sickly. Mrs. Steiner's health was also failing, to the point where she could no longer take care of herself properly.

Kathleen was Irish, a free person who had knowledge and skills pertaining to nursing. Although no great beauty, she did have lovely long red hair and a pretty scattering of freckles. She also had a warm smile and a vibrant personality, and they all loved to hear her lilting accent. But it was Dutch who soon took particular notice of her, and she of him. They were a contrast: the petite, fair-skinned Kathleen and the large, ruddy Dutch. Before long, a courtship began.

Ulrich was at the center of each encounter. Kathleen had no knowledge of German, and Dutch had little knowledge of English, so Ulrich became their translator. Every Sunday, the three of them would meet. Ulrich soon discovered that Dutch was not an expert at everything, as he had previously thought. When it came to courting, he was a little clumsy. Dutch wanted more words that would endear Kathleen to him, but Ulrich's knowledge of such words was limited. It really didn't matter, because Dutch and Kathleen soon fell in love.

A year passed, as did young Nia. Her death was no surprise, but it was still sad.

Mr. Steiner had full knowledge of the growing relationship between Kathleen and Dutch, and they soon told him they planned to marry. And so, after a two-month grieving period for his daughter, Mr. Steiner offered to give the bride away, with a big celebration to follow. It was obvious that Dutch had become the son Mr. Steiner had always wanted.

The wedding lasted all day, with more food than could be imagined, song, dance, and spirits. Although it was not Ulrich's first experience with drinking hard cider, he consumed more on this wedding day than ever before, maybe a little too much. He was happy for Dutch. It had been years since Ulrich had experienced so much fun and laughter, and it seemed to fill a void in his heart. He hoped it would not be the last time he felt that way.

There was extra laughter that day because during the wedding ceremony, Ulrich and many others heard Dutch's real name for the first time. It was Hendrick Slottheimer. This became cause for much kidding, with Kathleen saying she could not believe her name was now Mrs. Slottheimer.

CHAPTER 25

STEINER'S DAUGHTER AND HER BOYS

Mr. Steiner had decided that his grandsons, Gunter and Alfred, were old enough at ten and eight to start learning about the business of farming. He moved them into the cabin with Ulrich and told Ulrich to be their instructor.

"Teach them as you were taught by Dutch," he said. "You are up to the job."

Ulrich assured Mr. Steiner that he would do his best. He was excited that Mr. Steiner had picked him to train the boys, that Mr. Steiner had that much confidence in him.

Ulrich was excited to teach the boys the survival skills that Dutch had taught him: hunting, fishing, tracking, trapping, shooting. How to cut wood, tie ropes, and skin and tan hides. His mind was racing over all the things he had been taught. Of course, there were also the mundane matters they would need to learn: plowing, planting, stripping tobacco, mending fences, clearing woods, cutting and baling hay, milking cows, feeding and slopping pigs and slaughtering them when the time came. There was much to teach, and he was willing, excited, and capable of doing so. It gave him a new outlook on his life; it seemed a passage into adulthood.

The boys soon became his shadows, following him everywhere except to the outhouse—though sometimes they would be standing there when he came out!

Teaching them was the easy part. Keeping them safe was a little more difficult. Like most boys their age, they were mischievous, curious, and unafraid. They climbed the highest trees, swam in the pond even though they hardly knew how to swim, and explored the woods without Ulrich or the dogs.

One day, they wandered off and found a beehive. When Ulrich saw them, they were running for all they were worth toward him and the cabin. The bees were swarming all about, repeatedly stinging them. The outhouse was the closest structure, and Ulrich and the boys all headed in there.

The bees were in no hurry to leave, it seemed. It was crowded in the outhouse, and the smell was pretty bad, but it was better than getting stung. Finally, the bees left, and Ulrich took the boys to the cabin and treated their bites with a mud paste that Dutch had showed him how to make. Mr. Steiner and Paulina were none too happy with Ulrich for letting the boys out of his sight, but they were glad it wasn't any worse.

The worst day happened when Ulrich and the boys were doing some night fishing. They were having a good night, getting lots of bites; the pond was full of catfish, bream, and even some bass and crappie. But they were fishing with nightcrawlers and on the bottom; they were after catfish. They already had several on a stringer and were about to go in, but the boys wanted to catch one more apiece. Gunter, the older of the two, was standing a few yards down the bank, away from the fire, when Ulrich heard him holler.

"Something is crawling up my trouser leg!"

Looking down at the barefoot boy, Ulrich saw the tail of a water moccasin disappearing. He had to think quickly.

"Do not move, Gunter!" he said. "Just take a deep breath."

He continued to talk to Gunter as he slowly edged forward. He could see tears running down Gunter's cheeks. Ulrich knew the snake could not strike in an uncoiled position trapped inside the trouser leg, but if Gunter panicked and the snake fell to the ground, it would definitely bite the boy.

"Just stand very still, Gunter," Ulrich said again. To soothe Gunter, he lied, "It's probably just a black or bull snake, not dangerous, but still, you don't want to scare it."

Ulrich could see the outline of the snake. He drew the knife his father had given him and was ready to cut. The knife was razor-sharp, and it would only take one swipe to cut the snake in half. He thought maybe he should grab it toward the head, through Gunter's breeches, and then slice it in half.

It was a tense moment. The boy was crying; Ulrich was in a cold sweat. One more step and he would be in striking distance. He knew he only had one opportunity. While he knew water moccasin bites were rarely fatal, they could cause serious and ongoing illness and injury. He would be punished severely if he allowed harm to come to Gunter. But mostly, he was fond of the boy and didn't wish to see him hurt.

Luckily, the snake had done enough exploring and decided to leave. It dropped to the ground and crawled off. Gunter was still frozen. Ulrich went over, put his arms around him, and told him how brave he was. It was just a small snake, but to Gunter it must have seemed six feet long.

Sometimes things just turn out fine. They did that night; they were all safe and had ten nice-sized blue channel catfish on their stringer. When they got back, they cleaned and cooked three of them and enjoyed eating them in front of the cabin fireplace. Leftover cornbread and some beans were on the stove from earlier; it was a good supper. They put the rest of the fish on the stringer in the stream by the cabin to keep them alive. The next morning, they cooked three more for breakfast, and Ulrich sent the boys to give the others to Dutch and Big John.

They all agreed not to tell about the snake; they would keep that story to themselves.

As with most boys, adventure, wrestling, and playing games were more important to Gunter and Alfred than chores, and Ulrich let them enjoy those parts of growing up. He liked them, and he liked spending time with them. Also, he got to know their mother, Paulina; she was the most generous and outgoing of all the Steiner family.

There were days when, with pails in hand, Paulina would gather them all together, saying, "Come on, boys! The berries are just waiting to be picked so that your mama can make you some of the best jam in the county." They had no choice but to go; however, it was well worth the effort. In a few days Ulrich would be spreading some of that jam on his corn cakes.

It seemed Paulina was always needing for them to do something with her: berry or fruit picking, gathering black walnuts or wild mushrooms. Any reason for her to spend time with her boys. Ulrich enjoyed her company, and the extra food he was given was much appreciated.

And Paulina gave him a greater gift: the gift of education. Ulrich's education up until then had come in bits and pieces and in strange ways. Once, the man behind the counter at the general store had wrapped Ulrich's purchases in newspaper, and from that time on, Ulrich always asked for his items to be wrapped in newspaper or any paper with words. Back on the farm, he would read each word over and over, checking it against the phrasebook Matilda had given him, trying to understand the meaning.

But it wasn't until Paulina came back to the main house that he truly learned English well. She was an educated woman and was already teaching her sons to speak, read, and write in English; when she realized how eager Ulrich was to learn, she was happy to help him. Whenever he had spare time, he would practice what she was teaching him. They had many good laughs about how he thought a word should sound. Certain words just didn't look like they sounded in English. He couldn't understand how "tion" could be pronounced "shun" or how "gh" could sound like "f." In English, the person was placed before what he was doing; in German, it was just the opposite. But eventually, after much hard work, Ulrich could speak English fairly fluently and read and write it adequately.

The boys were proud of their English skills, and sometimes when they were around their grandfather Steiner, they would surprise him by speaking English. Mr. Steiner was impressed but cautious, because one of his ploys was to speak English when he didn't want others to know what he was saying, like the time he'd told the story about the "deal" he'd gotten when he'd bought young Ulrich's indenture contract.

Ulrich still wondered whether his father had realized just how long Ulrich would have to serve to complete his indenture.

CHAPTER 26

BOYS AND DOGS

Ulrich's life with the boys continued over the next few years. They played hard, but they also worked hard. They fished, hunted, trapped, skinned and tanned hides, tended the garden, and helped with the harvesting. Soon they were not little boys anymore, especially Gunter. By 1764, he was thirteen years old, practically a grown man in that time and place. And Ulrich would soon be leaving; in only months he would be a free man.

In December of 1764, with Christmas in the air, they attended services in a church decorated with greens, holly, and mistletoe. Ulrich knew little about attending church; he had not been to church since he was ten years old, when he had left the old country. However, he knew the boys' mother wanted them all to attend that day. The boys didn't want to go, but Ulrich told them that if they went and sang the Christmas carols, he would take them and the dogs hunting that afternoon.

So that afternoon after church they headed out with their guns and the dogs, Blau—the German word for blue—and Bruno.

Ulrich told the boys, "It's time you learn how to cook Mr. Dutch's favorite meal. We need rabbits."

The dogs were good hunters; with the snow on the ground, they would be needed even more, because the rabbits would be hunkered down.

They had barely gotten to the field by the woods when Blau started sniffing around a pile of branches. Soon, two rabbits jumped out. One went one way and one went the other. Ulrich, with his double-barreled gun, took one down immediately, but the one the boys fired at, with their less-powerful, single-barrel fowling guns, kept going. Bruno chased the second rabbit. Ulrich was gutting the first rabbit when Bruno came carrying the other one, who had been hit but had kept running. Each of the boys argued that it was his shot that hit the rabbit. No one would ever know that answer, so Ulrich told them it was probably both of their shots that brought it down.

They got three more rabbits and a pheasant before the day was over. That night they would cook the hasenpfeffer. As he had told Ulrich so long before, Dutch told the boys that real hasenpfeffer required a hare, not a rabbit.

"A hare has strong red meat and a rabbit mild, light meat," he said.

Then, also as before, he went into how hasenpfeffer was prepared "in the old country."

They proceeded to fix the German stew. Dutch had shown Ulrich many times how to prepare it. First they salted and marinated the rabbit; then they stewed it for about two hours. They used pheasant broth for additional flavor and added butter, salt, some herbs from the garden, and plenty of black pepper. Not having wine, Ulrich added a couple of spoonsful of shine.

Dutch had always said that hasenpfeffer was better if you let it sit for a day, but Ulrich and the boys were all too hungry to wait. They enjoyed some of it that night. The next day they invited Dutch and Big John over after work for a feast of the rest of the hasenpfeffer along with potatoes, green onions, radishes, and cornbread. For their dessert, they had some Christmas cakes made by Mrs. Steiner, who always made enough for the church, the family, and the farmhands.

Big John couldn't say enough about how much he enjoyed the meal. Dutch acknowledged it but then grumbled something about the "old country," though he didn't leave any in his bowl. He did compliment Ulrich, though, and said he was doing a good job with the boys.

Alfred, the younger boy, named after his grandfather on his mother's side, was a handful. He was full of adventure and loved the outdoors. Ulrich had to keep an eye on him and forbid him and his brother from going into the woods alone, especially after their rabbit hunting trip, where Ulrich had seen, in the distance, a black bear. Usually black bears are not aggressive unless they are females with cubs or males during mating season. The size of the one he spotted told him that it was a female. He was surprised to see her; most were in hibernation by that time of year. At any rate, he didn't want the boys walking up on her, and he warned them not to go into the woods alone.

However, his worst fear was realized when the bear came to the cabin instead. Blau and Bruno were going crazy, barking uncontrollably. He grabbed his rifle and ran outside. About seventy-five yards away stood Alfred, with his back to Ulrich, and twenty-five yards in front of Alfred stood the black bear.

Alfred was frozen, which was good. It gave Ulrich time to get closer. The bear was moving back and forth; she seemed confused, probably scared by all the noise the dogs were making. She was young and small, maybe 175 pounds; a large male can weigh up to 500 pounds. She just snorted, pawed the ground, and eventually turned and went back into the woods. To Ulrich's relief, they never saw her after that one incident.

Soon, though, they faced a more difficult situation. For a day or two, Ulrich had noticed Blau not eating all his food and seeming to be aloof and lazy. That was unusual, especially on the days the boys would come, which now was almost every day. Blau didn't seem excited to see them and had no desire to run when he had a chance.

"Ulrich, what's wrong with Blau?" Gunter asked. "He seems sad."

"Probably nothing," Ulrich assured him. "He will come around."

But the next day was one of the saddest days of all the time Ulrich spent on the Steiner farm. He and the boys were coming from the field just before dark when he noticed Blau, whom he had tied up that morning, acting strangely. Right away, Ulrich thought something was not right. Blau was staggering around in circles, seeming completely disoriented. When Ulrich went over to check on him, Blau started to growl and snarl as if he would attack and bite Ulrich. That is when Ulrich noticed how the dog's lower jaw just seemed to be hanging there and how he was drooling and foaming at the mouth. He seemed to have trouble moving his hind legs, and his muscles twitched.

Not sure what was going on, Ulrich sent for Dutch. Within the hour he was there. Again, Blau growled and became aggressive. Without saying anything, Dutch walked to his wagon and picked up his rifle. Then he walked back and, without warning, shot Blau in the head, killing him instantly.

"No!" Alfred screamed. "Why did you kill my Blau?"

He tried to run toward Dutch and the dead animal, crying uncontrollably, but Ulrich stopped him. Gunter just turned and walked inside, and Ulrich followed, still holding onto Alfred. Dutch came in behind them.

"Blau was sick," he told the boys, "with a disease called rabies. It is an incurable disease that causes the animal much pain, unbearable pain. It is best to put the animal out of its misery as soon as possible. I'm sorry you had to witness this, but Blau was not only sick and in pain but very dangerous. One day you will understand. We will get you another dog soon."

Dutch put his arm around Alfred and hugged him, looking at Gunter and asking if he was all right. Gunter did not reply; he just nodded. Dutch told him to take care of his brother and said that he would explain everything to Mr. Steiner. He told them to go get in the wagon; he would take them home. He placed his hand on Ulrich's shoulder as he was leaving.

That was a sad night, but generally, Ulrich's time with the boys was happy. The truth was that they brought new life to the farm and to Ulrich. Had they not been there, Ulrich's life would have been lonely those last few years of his indenture. They made it fun. Many times, Ulrich compared their lives to his life at their age. He hoped they would never have to know what it was like not to be free; he hoped they would always have plenty to eat, a family who loved them, and a bright future.

As it came near time for him to leave the Steiner farm, however, Ulrich was thinking more of his own future. He didn't want to end up like Dutch. Dutch seemed happy, but working on a farm that belonged to someone else was not for Ulrich. And he wanted to see more of the world. On Ulrich's visits to town, he had already decided that his life would not be one on the farm.

CHAPTER 27

ULRICH SAYS GOODBYE

Freedom grew nearer for Ulrich, and he marked off each day until finally it arrived. The day before he was to leave, Mr. Steiner and Dutch approached him with papers in hand, and he finally heard the words he had longed for.

"Ulrich," said Mr. Steiner, "I know you have been waiting a long time for me to hand you these freedom papers. You have grown into a fine young man. You deserve the opportunity to have something that belongs to you. But Dutch and I would like for you to stay on here, if you want to."

Dutch was smiling as Mr. Steiner spoke. Ulrich's heart pounded, because in front of him stood two men he respected, but his need to know more of the world overpowered him.

"Mr. Steiner, I appreciate the offer and the fact that you have always been fair to me," he said nervously. "However, this farm is all I have known for the past eleven years . . . I want to know more, to see more. I hope you understand."

He could feel the sweat running down his back as he anticipated their reply. He was relieved when Mr. Steiner said, "I do understand, Ulrich. Whatever your destiny may bring you, may it be blessed. God be with you."

He then shook Ulrich's hand, gave him his papers, and said to Dutch, "Tomorrow, take Ulrich to the city. He is now a free man."

As Mr. Steiner was walking away, Ulrich called to him in English, "Mr. Steiner, God be with you also." Steiner turned back in surprise, then smiled and nodded.

Ulrich was glad that the boys and their mother had gone to visit with Paulina's sister in town. It would have been hard to say so many goodbyes at once. Both the boys had already thanked him and let him know how much they appreciated him not telling on them for all the trouble they had caused.

The next morning, in the wagon, Dutch handed Ulrich a knapsack with enough food items to get him through the week. He also handed Ulrich two pence, saying they were from Mr. Steiner and would pay for a place to sleep for the first few nights.

Then, to Ulrich's surprise, Dutch told him that before he left the area, Ulrich would need to record the deed to some land that he was being given by Mr. Steiner. Ulrich didn't understand. Why would he receive land, when it was well known that indentured servants were no longer being given property with their freedom? Dutch's only reply was that Mr. Steiner had said Ulrich had earned the land.

"You will thank Mr. Steiner in years to come," Dutch said.

When they reached Philadelphia, it was hard to say goodbye. The knowledge that he was always welcome back on the farm made it easier for Ulrich. He thanked Dutch for all he had done to help him, and they reminisced for a few minutes.

"Do you remember me doing the woodchopping and how you would say, 'This will make you strong like an ox?'" Ulrich asked.

Finally, Ulrich climbed off the wagon and reached up to shake hands with Dutch.

"Thank Kathleen for all the food she fixed for me," he said. "Now get back to the farm and start producing those babies you always wanted!"

They both laughed as Dutch rode away.

Sometimes sadness and excitement walk hand in hand. That day Ulrich experienced both.

CHAPTER 28

ULRICH LEAVES THE FARM

And so Ulrich's freedom began.

Every time he walked down the street in those first few days, embracing the sights, he was in awe of everything that he saw. This was the first time he had been to Philadelphia by himself, the first time he'd stayed more than a few hours. It was quite a contrast to the farm and the cabin. While on the farm, he'd had interactions with only a few people, and now there were so many walking about. It was a new whole world. Now he would really get to see America.

However, after a week of looking for work, he was still unemployed. His food and money were almost gone.

Suddenly, his luck changed. As he stood in front of a stocking shop, a man in a wagon pulled up and started gathering boxes and taking them inside the store. After watching a couple of trips, Ulrich decided to help, thinking maybe the man might be glad and hire him to help with other deliveries as well.

The man seemed pleased to have the extra hands, so as he was leaving, Ulrich spoke up.

"Sir, would you be in need of someone to help make deliveries?"

"Sorry," the man said. "I only had this one. But tell me, what is your name?"

"Ulrich Kessler, sir," Ulrich said, sticking out his hand. "I'm a hard worker, and I'm looking for work."

The man shook Ulrich's hand and started asking him more questions, this time in German, as he had heard Ulrich's accent and he spoke German as well. Ulrich gave him a very short version of how he had come to America and of his life on the farm, saying that he had come to town to learn a trade now that he was a free man.

"My name is Hendrick Schmidt," the man said. "I operate a textile mill in Germantown and was making a delivery of thread stockings today. I come in every two weeks to make sure the shop is well stocked. Do you have any interest in the textile industry? If so, head northwest down this road to Germantown. It's about six miles, two hours by foot. The mill I operate is on the Wissahickon Creek. Ask anyone you see, and they will know who I am and how to find me. It is hard work, and you would be the lowest-paid worker until you learned the trade."

He also told Ulrich that the Germantown community was made up mainly of hardworking Quakers and Mennonites. "A young man like you could become successful in this industry if you are willing to work hard, as you said. The war has taken many of the young men, so there is a need for those who want to work."

"What war is that, sir, that you speak of?" asked Ulrich, who had not heard anything about a war.

"Why, the war between the English and French and some of the Indian tribes on each side," Mr. Schmidt replied. "Where have you been, boy? This war has been going on now for more than three years.

It's mostly been fought in the northern territories, but the Ohio Valley is being sought after by both sides. Fortunately, we here in Pennsylvania have been spared the fighting. However, taxes have been raised by the English on everything we buy from them, especially supplies such as sugar and tea. There is a growing bitterness among the colonists concerning these taxes. There has even been talk of a revolt."

Little did Ulrich realize that the taxes Schmidt had spoken of would not only change his life but all of history.

"All I want to do is learn a trade and earn an honest wage," replied Ulrich. "I own nothing, only my life. That is all I have to fight for. Since I am neither English nor French, I will leave this war to others. I just want to earn a living."

"Then," Mr. Schmidt said, "come see me tomorrow."

He smiled and bid Ulrich goodbye.

Excited, Ulrich was up early the next day and headed to Germantown, to his future and hopefully his first paying job. Finding Mr. Schmidt was easy, just as he had said it would be. Everybody knew him and where he could be found.

Ulrich could tell Mr. Schmidt was a little surprised to see him, but Mr. Schmidt was glad to help him get started. With his reference, Ulrich acquired a sleeping room that offered hot coffee and a biscuit in the morning and an evening meal after work.

Ulrich soon realized Mr. Schmidt was right when he said how difficult and challenging the textile industry was, especially for one just learning the trade. Ulrich worked long days, and the gluey starch that was used to hold and strengthen the fibers was smelly and hard to remove from his hands and clothing. Determined to learn more and work his way up, he kept at it, and he watched and listened to the seasoned weavers. They were always telling him how much easier working the loom was since the "flying shuttle" had been invented. Before its invention, a weaver needed an apprentice to help pass the shuttle, a task requiring much time. Now a single person could work the loom, making weaving more efficient.

It soon became apparent to Ulrich that Germantown was a thriving community and important to the area. He felt certain he had made the right decision in finding work and settling there. It seemed to him that the textile industry was growing every day. Farmers in the area could hardly keep up with the demand for hemp and flax as well as sheep's wool.

PART TWO

CHAPTER 29

ULRICH AND ANNA

As time passed, Ulrich started making friends with other weavers, in particular Otto Lowenstein. Otto was glad to give him instructions, since he was so eager to learn. Before long they became good friends, and Otto invited Ulrich to come to a Quaker worship service on Sunday and meet his family. Although in his early years and occasionally with the Steiners he had attended the Lutheran church, Ulrich knew nothing of the Quakers. Otto said he would be welcome anyway. He did explain that almost all who lived in Germantown were Quakers or Mennonites, mainly people of like mind who had been persecuted in the past for their beliefs and had then founded this community.

Ulrich's answer to the invitation came easily; he wanted and needed to belong somewhere. That Sunday, he put on his best outfit, which was not all that good but was all he had. Walking into the church, he was greeted by Otto and introduced to the rest of the family. They were all nice and hospitable, and he felt welcomed by them, but when he met Otto's sister Anna, words failed him. She was so pretty, and he was so nervous. Luckily, the service was about to begin, a relief.

After the service, Otto told Ulrich that the following Sunday, the family would like for him to join them at their home for supper. Of course, Ulrich said he would be there. As they parted, he looked Anna's way and saw a smile. It was slight, but it was all he needed.

Anxious to see Anna again, he was at the church that Sunday before any members arrived. He was mostly interested in impressing Anna, but he also wanted to make a good impression on Conrad Lowenstein, her father. Secretly, Ulrich thought Mr. Lowenstein might not be impressed if he knew Ulrich's eagerness was motivated more by seeing Anna than by attending services.

Many more Sundays followed. The thought of seeing Anna again got Ulrich through each week. When he did see her, he would smile at her and try to say something nice, like how lovely she looked, but he was clumsy and inexperienced in such things. She would just smile back, walk right past, and say, "Well, thank you, Mr. Kessler."

Soon, though, there was no doubt that Anna and Ulrich had a mutual attraction. More and more questions were being asked of Ulrich by Mr. Lowenstein. Ulrich left nothing out of his answers. He told how he came to America, how he lost his mother aboard the ship and his sister and father after arriving, and how he'd spent eleven years indentured to Mr. Steiner. It seemed that mentioning Mr. Steiner was to Ulrich's credit; Mr. Lowenstein had had some dealings with him and knew him to be a fair and honest man.

Mr. Lowenstein asked Ulrich whether he held any bitterness toward Mr. Steiner. He explained that the Quakers were a peaceful, God-loving community, that there was no room for anger. He talked of a rebellion by a man named Nathaniel Bacon, who had led a revolt of indentured servants against the Tidewater Aristocrats, burning down the city of Jamestown.

"The reason I'm telling you this is that we do not want angry men in our community," Mr. Lowenstein said.

"I hold no hatred in my heart toward any man, but especially not toward Mr. Steiner," Ulrich said. "He treated me fairly and let me live with my friend Dutch, who taught me many things about forgiveness and honesty and the value of hard work. I am not an angry man, Mr. Lowenstein. I will never dishonor you, Anna, or the community."

"If you wish to court Anna, you will have to assume our way of living and begin your preparations to become a Quaker," Mr. Lowenstein said. "Our lifestyle is different from that of the outside world; it will take some adjusting. Ulrich, are you prepared to be a willing and faithful servant?"

Of course, all Ulrich could think about was being with Anna, so he was ready to agree to any commitment. And with that commitment began his induction into the Quaker community and his courtship of Anna.

CHAPTER 30

ANNA'S STORY

Also on that day, the rules of the courtship were laid out. There was always to be a chaperone with Anna and Ulrich. The person assigned to this duty was Anna's great-aunt, Abigail. She was stone deaf and had poor eyesight, and she nodded off frequently. Anna's mother had asked Abigail to be the chaperone, perhaps wanting to give Anna and Ulrich a bit of privacy; Anna thanked her for it. And so, always with Great-Aunt Abigail following behind, Ulrich and Anna began walking and visiting together, and Anna told him about her life.

Anna was a good Quaker girl, and as with most girls at the time, her main purpose in life was to learn how to serve her future husband: cooking, cleaning, caring for children, and maintaining household order. Her main teacher was her mother, who managed their household.

However, each Quaker community designated a leader, called the primer, and with the help of the congregation's elders—all male—he made all the moral decisions. What he considered good or bad was the law and was followed by all the others. Anna's father, Mr. Lowenstein, was the primer in Germantown. He was highly respected; his family had come over from the Prussian city of Krefeld and had been one of the original families who founded the settlement.

When Anna married, she knew she would be a *feme covert*, with all power over her life transferred to her husband. For years, she had been in no hurry. But now, at age seventeen, she had started considering marriage, and now she had found a man she would be proud and happy to marry.

Before long, Ulrich met with Anna's father and made a formal request for her hand. In the Quaker community, young women were allowed to marry whomever they chose; they could not have marriage forced on them. However, if a woman was not yet twenty-one, her father had to assent to the marriage. Anna's father was not an easy person to get past; however, he assented, with the stipulation that Ulrich must formally join the Quaker congregation before the wedding. Ulrich agreed with most Quaker principles and felt a definite kinship with the people living in the community, and he accepted gladly. Ulrich had also finished his apprenticeship and was earning full wages, enabling the couple financially to be on their own, a requirement for all those wishing to marry in the Quaker community.

Anna's mother and sisters started making her wedding quilt and selected foods they would prepare for the meal after the service. A house had been found, and everything they needed to set up housekeeping would be provided. Ulrich was ready to make Anna his bride, and she was ready to be Ulrich's wife and mother to the children they would make together.

A few weeks later, at worship, Anna and Ulrich stood in front of the congregation and announced their intention to marry. A placard with the announcement would be posted for all to see. Before the wedding could happen, many questions would be asked by the men to Ulrich and the women to Anna. Finally, the marriage was approved and the date set: May twenty-eighth. To Ulrich it was a special day; it was both his mother's birthday and the day they had boarded the ship to America. Now, more than ever, it was a date he would never forget.

The day of the wedding was solemn as Ulrich and Anna entered the church. Two chairs were sitting in front, facing out toward family and the congregation. They sat in the chairs during a long silence, and then they were asked to exchange promises. It was a simple, straightforward agreement between two people, with the congregation bearing witness.

"In the presence of God and these our friends," Anna said, "I take thee, Ulrich Kessler, to be my husband, promising with divine assistance to be unto thee a loving and faithful wife so long as we shall live."

Ulrich repeated the pledge to Anna, and they were ordained husband and wife in holy matrimony by the elders and the congregation.

Afterward, they signed the Quaker wedding certificate, as did all the congregation, giving witness to the ceremony. There was much handshaking, and goodwill offerings were given. After the ceremony, all the family went to the Lowenstein home for a meal before Anna and Ulrich departed to their new home.

Unlike at Dutch and Kathleen's wedding, there was no music, dancing, or cider. In Ulrich's heart, he wished there had been more celebration, but he never spoke of it. He had Anna as his wife, and that was all he needed.

After the meal, they left, ready to be completely alone. When they arrived at the house, they saw that all the furniture and household goods were already in place.

At first, they were hesitant about how everything should proceed, but soon passion took over, and the love they had for each other consumed them. Waking the next morning, still wrapped in each other's arms, led to more lovemaking.

There was no happier man than Ulrich. He had found a wife, a trade, and a community. He had everything he wanted; it was time to say goodbye to bitter memories.

CHAPTER 31

HANNAH, THE LOST SISTER

A few months after the wedding, Anna received a letter from a friend, saying that she would be stopping by to meet Anna's new husband. When the day came and Anna answered the knocking at the door, there stood a beautiful young woman with red hair. She held a baby in her arms, and a toddler clung to her skirts. A tall man with light brown hair and a weathered complexion, the sign of a man who spent most of his working hours outdoors, stood by her. Hugs and tears followed, and the two women were so involved with each other that they almost forgot about introductions to the rest of their families.

"Anna," said the young woman, "this is my husband, Sean Malone. This is our older child, Ben, and this is our baby daughter Abigail. We call her Abbie—all but Sean, that is. He prefers the name Abigail."

Anna was about to reply when a strange look came over her friend's face. She was looking past Anna into the house, staring at Ulrich, who had just walked into the room.

"I'm sorry," she said to Ulrich. "It's rude to stare. For a minute you reminded me of someone."

Then there was a long pause as their eyes held. His complexion turned pale, and she looked as if she were frozen in time. It seemed forever before words were spoken.

"My name is Hannah," she said. "My papa's name was Johann. My mama's was Matilda. She died on the ship coming to America. My brother's name was Ulrich; he was taken from us when he was ten years old. I haven't seen him since. Is it you? Ulrich?"

With tears in his eyes, Ulrich said, "Yes, Hannah, it is me."

With that, they came together in a long embrace, holding each other, not wanting to let go. But soon they let go and began to talk. There was a lot of catching up to do, and Ulrich was anxious to hear what had happened to his sister and father after the day he was parted from them.

Anna busied herself making tea and setting the table with biscuits and jam, adding to the conversation by marveling that while she had known both Hannah's and Ulrich's stories, she had not known enough details about Hannah's to put the two together. Sean put Abbie to sleep on the bed, and then young Ben fell asleep in his arms. Sean laid the boy next to his sister and covered them with a quilt, then joined the others, where Hannah was just beginning to tell her story.

"I hardly know where to start, there is so much to tell," she said. "Ulrich, Papa was never the same after they took you from us that day. He blamed himself for Mama's death and for losing you. He knew you had the better chance of surviving alone, out of us two, but so many children had died on the ship, and he was not sure how strong you still were.

"We stayed on board for another whole week after they took you.

No one seemed to want a girl and a father. Some offered just to take me, but of course Papa refused. Finally, a landowner in Virginia bought us from the captain. So again we found ourselves on a boat, headed for a colony in the Chesapeake Bay area of Virginia. We were on the boat for the best part of two days, and upon arriving, we spent a day in a wagon, traveling to the plantation. Mostly the men spoke English, so we struggled to understand what they were saying. Once we arrived at the plantation, we were separated. Papa was taken to the tobacco quarters, where he would work and live for the next four years. I was taken to the domestic quarters.

"I rarely saw him; however, when I did, he was always concerned about my well-being. I said I was all right, but I always lied. It would have destroyed him to know the truth. He was sure you must hate him for letting you go, but he had made a promise to himself to bring us all back together. He thought perhaps we might be a happy family again somehow. To know the truth about me would have destroyed his dream, and the dream was all that kept him going.

"At first, I had felt privileged being in the house as a domestic, not having to endure some of the hardships I saw other indentured servants and slaves encounter. That is, until I realized the master of the house would be making visits to my bedroom. There was no one to tell, no one to help me. I had to make sure Papa never found out. I often thought of killing myself, but I had a strong will to live, and I knew that my death would also kill Papa. I reminded myself that compared to the conditions of many others, I was lucky.

"But it was bad, Ulrich, very bad. I was only fourteen and had no knowledge of men. The first night when the master came into my room and pulled my cover off me, I recoiled and sat up with my knees bent and my arms wrapped tight around them. He smelled of tobacco and whiskey and had an evil grin on his face. Even though I had heard rumors of his infamous visits, I could not believe it was happening to me. I begged him to please let me go back to sleep. But it was no use. He told me to either go along with his desires or he would send me to the fields, where the overseers would have their way with me and would not be as gentle. I knew that the overseers were worse than the master; they were both large, sturdy men and both of an ill nature. They had their way with the young slave girls, many receiving beatings or even being sold elsewhere, away from their families, when they resisted.

"And so I gave in. That first year his visits were frequent . . .

"Soon, even though Papa's contract was coming to an end, I had three more years on mine. My only thought was to survive. Hope was all I had. In our last meeting, Papa told me he was returning to Bucks County, Pennsylvania. He was being given a small parcel of land there as part of his indenture payment, part of the original contract. He was also being given a horse and some food. He told me he would work and save enough money to pay off the rest of my time, and he did. In a little over a year, he returned for me. It was the happiest day of my life."

CHAPTER 32

THE LIE

"I was almost free, but not completely," Hannah continued. "As part of my release, Papa had negotiated a deal with a man living in Germantown. I was to care for his children and perform household duties while his wife was recovering from being ill. He was willing to pay for my remaining two years of servitude. Ulrich, that man was Mr. Lowenstein, your father-in-law. Because of his offer, my life improved greatly. The Lowensteins and the other Quaker families were all kind and gentle people. Even though Anna here was much younger than I, we soon became close friends. Being part of the Quaker community was just what I needed. I was safe, and I was healing.

"But Papa's dream of uniting the family was fading. He explained to me that while in Philadelphia some months earlier, he had been asking where Mr. Steiner's farm was located, and at the general store, the owner had pointed out to him one of Mr. Steiner's sons-in-law, Dolf Stangl. Papa said he talked to the man and explained to him that he was looking for his son, whose indenture contract had been bought by Mr. Steiner. Mr. Stangl told him, 'Yes, I remember a boy coming to the farm a while back. He stayed for a couple of years but did not work out. He was difficult, so Steiner sold him off. He's been gone a long time. We have no idea where he is. Could have been sold again by now, but good luck in your search.' And then he walked away.

"After that, Papa was a sad and lonely man, though I tried my best to make him happy. After all, he had worked hard to help me find a better life.

"And my life was getting better all the time. Only a few weeks after arriving in Germantown, I had met Sean. Sean, who immigrated here from Ireland and was a blacksmith, came to Germantown once a week to make repairs, take orders, and shoe horses if needed. While making one of his calls to the house, he caught my eye, and I caught his. Before long, he seemed to be showing up more often. Then he asked Mr. Lowenstein for permission to spend time with me on my day off. Permission was granted, and before long our relationship became serious.

"Sean had a buggy, and often we would go for a ride in the country. On one such ride, in the spring, I felt especially close to Sean. I moved close to him and interlocked my arm with his as he guided the buggy over the path, through the fields alive with nature's beauty, all looking magnificent in the majestic show that they put on that time of year. We came upon a meadow by a stream that pooled into a small lake. We got out of the buggy, and as we walked hand in hand to the meadow, the smell of honeysuckle was in the air. All seemed well in life as we sat down on a blanket. It was serene. I was at peace with the world. Then Sean stood up, bent down on one knee, and asked me to marry him. I looked at him with tears in my eyes.

"'Sean, I love you,' I said, 'but there are things about me that you do not know, and once you do, I'm sure you will not want me. I think you should take me back to the Lowensteins' house now.'

"'Please talk to me, Hannah,' he said. 'Nothing matters about the past. I love you, and I want you to be my wife, the mother of my children.'

"But I felt he had to know. So that day, for the first time, I told the story of the abuse I had endured while being an indentured domestic. Sean sat and listened, without comment or interruption, for over an hour as I told him my story. I left nothing out: our homeland, the voyage, our mother's death, our separation, but mainly the two years I spent being raped by the master of the farm where I was working. He had to know everything.

"I also told him how living with the Quakers had taught me about forgiveness, how it frees one from a life of hatred, anger, and resentment that corrodes the vessel that carries it. Then I told him again that I did not expect him to marry me, that I would understand if he no longer wanted me.

"As we stood, he put his hands on my shoulders and looked at me with those steel-blue eyes of his. I was surprised to see that he was teary as well.

"Then he said, 'Hannah Kessler, I only hope that as we go through our life together as man and wife, you can teach me to become the type of person you are today.'

"And then, for the first time, he kissed me.

"Our marriage soon followed. And as you can see, we now have two children, Benjamin and Abigail.

"Now let me tell you about what happened to Papa. Soon after Sean and I became engaged, Papa asked me to go back to our homeland with him. He said he had worked odd jobs to save enough money to pay for our passage. He was lonely and yearned to return to the place where he had grown up; America had never fulfilled his dream, had never given him what he wanted. It had only taken most of what he loved away from him: Mama, his son, and his pride. I tried to explain to him that he would now have a home and live with me and Sean after we married. We could buy a small farm, and he could sell milk and cheese as he had in the old country.

"But Papa left without me. He moved close to Mama's brother. I prayed that he was happy and well. I wrote to him occasionally, but I never heard back. As you know, Papa could barely read or write. But his brother's wife wrote to me last year and told me Papa died. She thought he died of a broken heart, never having recovered from losing his family.

"As fate would have it, Sean and I didn't stay long in the Philadelphia area after Father left. Blacksmiths are much in demand, and an old friend from Ireland who had migrated to Boston was begging Sean or his brother to set up shop with him. So we began our new life in Boston, which has truly been wonderful.

"The reason we are back in this area is because Sean's brother, Evan, recently died, leaving only his wife and daughter. Evan's widow needed help with selling his shop. Everything is settled now, and I wanted to visit Anna before going back to Boston. I had heard she was now married, and I wanted to meet her husband.

"What a wonderful surprise to find that my long-lost brother is married to my dear and loving friend! Oh, Ulrich, Papa and Mama would be so happy for us. We could both have gone to our graves never knowing the other was alive. Now we do know. It is truly a gift from God."

As Hannah's story ended, they continued to talk into the night, with tears flowing from time to time. The next day, as Sean and Hannah departed, brother and sister made promises that they would write to each other often.

That night, as Ulrich and Anna lay together, they reflected on all that had happened. The visit had brought back many memories, some good and some painful. It had been a time for healing, a time to be treasured.

CHAPTER 33

1775: Leaving Germantown for Lancaster

Around the year 1750, imports of textiles had become expensive, and the colonies were moving toward being more self-sufficient in making fabric. Germantown had become one of the leading manufactures of textiles. Then, with the invention of the spinning jenny in 1764, every homemaker could spin, giving the weavers limitless thread for production.

While living in Germantown, Ulrich fared very well. He was by no means a wealthy man, but his family lived a comfortable life. He and Anna had three children, all healthy and active.

The community had grown and thrived; however, Ulrich could see changes occurring, making life more difficult. The Stamp Act imposed by the British created financial hardships through excessive taxes. Differences were raging between the Tories, who were loyal to King George, and the Patriots, who wanted independence from the British. In 1774, the Continental Congress was established, forming a new government.

It seemed the fighting and the taxation were destroying everything good. At one time in Germantown, stocking weavers had been in high demand, producing as many as sixty thousand pairs of stockings per year and selling them at one dollar a pair. Now, almost daily, weavers were being let go. Everyone was unsure of what the future would bring.

Then Pennsylvania passed a "war tax." Anyone who did not pay it would have his property confiscated as payment. This put the Germantown community, which was still mostly Quaker, in a bad place. Quakers rejected the paying of any taxes, and their religious beliefs forbade any form of physical violence. Most Quakers and Mennonites would assist and give comfort to any wounded, hungry, or sick soldiers, whether British or Patriots. However, unwilling to support the violence of war, few wanted to give loyalty to either group.

Ulrich was a loyal Quaker, and in many ways he admired the anti-war stance of the church. But he had primarily become a Quaker for Anna's sake, and unlike most other Quakers, he was not a pacifist. War, he thought, should be avoided whenever possible, but this war was necessary. Having spent so many years under indenture, Ulrich knew only too well how it felt to be in bondage. He did not want his family, friends, and neighbors to serve a tyrant.

Ulrich decided to talk to the church elders to see whether any compromise could be made. He suggested a donation of canvas cloth or inexpensive blankets to the Patriots. Discussions went on for days, with even more suggestions, but to no avail. The elders refused to budge. They would not allow the congregation to participate in the war effort. Ulrich knew that a small number of Quakers had abandoned these religious convictions to fight for liberty; they were called Free

Quakers. But the price they paid was expulsion from the church. He did not want that for himself or his family.

Very soon afterward, Ulrich made a decision to leave Germantown and move his family to Lancaster, Pennsylvania, where they would live and farm on the twenty-five acres which had been given to him by Mr. Steiner. Anna's brother Otto and his family would go to Lancaster with them, while her parents and other siblings headed to Ohio. He was happy, as was Anna, that Otto and his family were coming with them. Besides being an accomplished weaver, Otto was skilled in cabinetry and metalwork. Lancaster had become a hub for artisans and craftsmen, boasting some three hundred living in the area. It would suit them all well.

CHAPTER 34

Chance Meeting with Dutch

A few days before leaving Germantown to go to Lancaster, Ulrich was in town to buy supplies. As he walked past the Tun Tavern, where he and Dutch had always eaten when Dutch brought him to town, he looked in the window. There sat the man to whom he owed his life— the man who had saved his life—Dutch Slottheimer.

Ulrich entered the tavern and walked toward Dutch. Dutch looked up but showed no signs of recognizing Ulrich; after all, it had been many years.

"*Guten Tag*, Dutch," Ulrich said.

When Dutch heard Ulrich's voice, he immediately jumped to his feet.

"Ulrich!" he exclaimed. "My curious little friend! It is good to see you. How long has it been?"

"Much too long," Ulrich replied. "We need to do some catching up."

The men's coffee cups were filled over and over as Dutch told Ulrich all that had happened with the Steiner family. Mrs. Steiner, he said, had died unexpectedly in her sleep. She had been ill, but death had come sooner than anyone had expected. It was good that Paulina and her boys were still living in the main house with Mr. Steiner. Then Dutch told Ulrich about his own family.

"At first, we didn't think we were ever going to have children. That all changed when we were blessed with Michael, who is now ten. His sister Regina is eight and is pretty like her mother. You know, Kathleen is an Irish girl and wanted to give the children Irish names. So they have Irish first names and a German surname. It's all right, though, because more often than not, people refer to Michael as Little Dutch. He is a good shot, almost as good as his father! He also loves the farm, says it is in his blood. Both children speak German as well as English, although not as well as I would prefer.

"Ulrich, remember how I told you to keep trying, no matter how hard things got, and to always try to do the right thing, no matter how tempting it was to take the shorter route? Well, that paid off for me: Mr. Steiner made me a landowner. He deeded many acres over to me and my family; it was a great day in my life! I finally had my own farm.

"Of course, all of this was dampened by the war. Mr. Steiner and I want the Patriots to win, but many in our area are still loyal to the king. We are careful, as you should be, not to express our loyalties to just anyone. A government is being formed as we speak; so far, we have been left alone. But some Patriot troops started crossing our land, and Mr. Steiner agreed to let the troops fish, hunt, and set up camp on the north end of the property where it adjoins Mr. Gerber's farm; Mr. Gerber is also in favor of independence. We leave the soldiers alone and, according to Mr. Steiner, they keep us safe. While that may be true, my rifle is never far from my reach.

"Paulina's boys are grown now. Gunter talks constantly of joining the militia; many young men we know have already done so. This talk does not make his mother happy. She is convinced Gunter will do something foolish; these are troubling times. Alfred has married and has produced one grandchild, with another on the way.

"But enough about me and the Steiners. Tell me, Ulrich, what brings you to town today, and how have you fared since leaving the farm?"

Ulrich began, telling Dutch about meeting Mr. Schmidt and starting work at his textile factory, about becoming a Quaker, about meeting and marrying Anna.

"Now," Ulrich went on, "we have a son and two daughters, and Anna is with child again. She is a wonderful mother and, like your Kathleen, a warm and giving person.

"While I am not a wealthy person, I have prospered and am now considered a master weaver. Over the years, I have apprenticed many into the textile industry. However, just in the past year, we have had to let many stocking weavers go due to increased taxes, lack of supplies, and rumors of the British taking Germantown.

"Many families are leaving the area. Most of Anna's relatives are leaving for Ohio. But her brother Otto and his family are coming to Lancaster, Pennsylvania, with us and with other Quaker families. We will start new businesses there and live together on the twenty-five acres Mr. Steiner gave me. Dutch, I know you had something to do with that; I will always be grateful. Other Quaker families will join us there soon, and together we will put up our barns and houses and look after one another.

"And I have one other piece of news: I'm glad to tell you that I reunited with my sister Hannah. Soon after we were married, Anna received a letter from a dear friend who said she and her family planned to visit us on their way to Boston. The friend turned out to be Hannah; Anna had never realized the connection between us. Even after so many years, Hannah recognized me right away, and after a moment—she had been a little girl when I'd seen her last—I knew her as well.

"Ours was a brief visit but a joyful one. And it was an important one, Dutch, because when she told me her story, I realized our father had never abandoned me as I had thought. You see, as soon as Papa was released from his indenture, he came to collect Hannah. She was in a terrible situation until then, but Papa was able to arrange for her to pay off the remainder of her indenture working for Anna's family, the Lowensteins. That was how she and Anna met. Papa's plan was to find me too, so that we could all be together again, but when he encountered Dolf in town and asked about me, Dolf told him I was no longer at the Steiner farm, that no one knew where I had gone. Dolf must have lied on purpose, just to hurt me."

Dutch shook his head, his mouth an angry line, but said nothing.

"And now we will never be reunited," Ulrich continued sadly, "because Papa returned to Germany and then passed away.

"But though I have lost both my parents now, I still have Hannah, and I rejoice that she is alive and has a happy family of her own. And Anna's and my fourth child will be born in Lancaster, a symbol of renewal and of our new home there.

"For certain, let the Steiner family know of all that I have told you and that I think of them often. Perhaps one day our paths will cross again. I'm glad I picked this day to make my last trip to town for supplies. I send best wishes of a long and happy life back to Kathleen, to your children, and of course, always to you. You replaced my father when I so desperately needed one. I will always be grateful and will never forget. I've even told my children all about you. You are like a legend to them—and to me."

Both men rose from their chairs. They realized a handshake was not enough. No, they had a bond that time and circumstance could never break. So it was bear hugs and many good wishes for the future, hoping that one day after all the warring was over, they would meet again.

CHAPTER 35

LANCASTER

In March of 1775, the families packed their belongings into wagons and began their trip. It took ten days, two more than they had anticipated, because of the rutted, muddy roads. When they finally arrived, they were tired and dirty, but when Ulrich looked at Anna and her reaction to their new land, he knew they had done the right thing. The land was better than they had expected: rich soil, pristine, as if no animals or people had been on it. The overall landscape was overwhelmingly beautiful. As they walked the land, they discovered a clear running creek full of fish, wooded areas that would provide plenty of firewood, and just the right spot for the barn, which would hold their loom.

"This is breathtaking," Anna said. "Ulrich, right where we stand is a perfect place to build our new home."

That night as they lay awake, they gave thanks to the Almighty and then to Mr. Steiner and Dutch for making this possible.

They began the process of making a new life. The garden was put in, along with a chicken coop, a smokehouse, a wood storage area, and makeshift pens and fences. Before winter was upon them, there would be many "house raisings," with all able-bodied men and boys taking part. Until then, they would camp outside with their wagons as they had on the journey.

Soon, Anna and Ulrich's son Daniel was born, and they learned that Otto's wife Emma was going to have another child. All in all, they would soon be a family of fourteen.

Eventually, they built two houses, fenced in to form a small Quaker village.

Because Otto and Ulrich were like-minded about the war, they made the decision to support the Patriots. They let it be known that Patriot troops could pass freely across their land, fish, water their horses from the stream and graze them in any fallow fields. They supplied much-needed corn, beans, and eggs to the Patriots from their farm. Otto's carpentry and metalworking skills were in demand for the army's needs, and Ulrich could not keep up with the demand for blankets.

During the war years, Otto and Ulrich became known and respected as master craftsmen. Otto's six children and Ulrich's four were cousins but were as close as brothers and sisters. It was the men's hope that one day their sons would take over their businesses. They all prospered, and life was good.

But the war years also brought strife to Lancaster in ways that would change the town and the lives of the families.

CHAPTER 36

THE HESSIAN BOY

In September of 1777, Lancaster was made the capital of the United States due to the British occupation of Philadelphia. The capital was soon moved to York, and Lancaster became a hub for prisoners of war. Several thousand British prisoners were sent to Lancaster, where they were put into huge stockades. Hessian prisoners, who were from Germany but fought on the side of the British, were sent to Lancaster also, because of the number of German-speaking residents. Officers were sometimes paroled to live in rented quarters among the townspeople. Some were even kept in taverns and private homes.

Many of the prisoners were given work to support the war effort, such as guarding supplies and making cannons, shot, rifle barrels, and shoes for Washington's troops. Downtown Lancaster had a military barracks, stable, warehouse, and powder house to support the needs of the Patriot troops.

One day, while making a delivery, Ulrich came upon two Patriot soldiers who had their rifles pointed at a kneeling Hessian prisoner, a boy no older than seventeen. It seemed someone had been stealing supplies from the warehouse, and the militia men had been sent there to find the offender and execute him on the spot. They had caught the boy with a hundred-pound bag of beans. The boy was begging, in German, that he had stolen nothing.

The soldiers, it appeared, could not understand German, so Ulrich stopped and asked if he could help.

"We need no help," one of the soldiers said. "This man was caught stealing and will be executed. We have our orders."

"But he says he didn't steal the beans. What if he is innocent?" Ulrich asked.

The soldiers looked away. They said nothing.

"What is your name?" Ulrich asked the boy in German.

"Hahn Gasometer," replied the boy, adding, "I did not steal! I was walking around the warehouse, as is my job, when I noticed a window that was partially opened, with footprints leading away. I believe the window was left open by someone who was going to return later and that the beans were placed by the window for easy removal after dark. I was returning the beans to the front of the warehouse, to stack them with the other bags for shipment to the troops."

At Ulrich's insistence, he and Hahn went to the back of the warehouse, the soldiers following. There they saw the open window.

"This proves nothing," one of the soldiers said. "He probably was the one who opened the window. He will be shot. It is a most serious crime to steal from the army. Our troops are in great need of food. Some are starving in the field while vermin like this creature are safe and well-fed. We have been among them, and we know. I say we shoot him right now, and good riddance!"

These men had been to war and knew the devastation of it; they had watched their fellow Patriots suffer and die in battle and from disease, frostbite, and starvation. Ulrich understood their anger, but he remembered what Dutch had once told him: *Do not be in a hurry for revenge.*

Ulrich asked the men if they would wait until morning to execute Hahn. He told them they could put Hahn in the barricade and watch the window that night to see whether anyone returned for the beans. They agreed to wait until sunrise, but they said that at first light they would come for the boy and he would be shot.

That night, the soldiers and Ulrich sat in the dark and waited. The soldiers were drinking rum and fell asleep around midnight. Ulrich noticed movement at the window and nudged the soldiers; they were groggy but plenty alert to realize what was happening. Ulrich recognized the man in the shadows right away. It was John Crass. He and his brother Jacob had been suspected of rustling livestock from the local farmers for years, but no one had been able to prove it.

The soldiers apprehended John Crass and made him tell them the truth. It seemed that Jacob was working inside the warehouse and was placing beans, sugar, tea, and more where John could get it at night. Then they would sell it at a good price.

And so there was an execution the next morning, but it wasn't Hahn. The two brothers died at the firing squad wall on the outside of town. Three more soldiers and an officer joined the two soldiers who had watched and waited with Ulrich; all fired at once, and the brothers died instantly. Military justice was swift and final.

CHAPTER 37

GUNTER

One day in December, Ulrich was at the general store, loading his wagon with supplies, when two young army recruits walked by.

"Good day to you," he said.

"Good day to you, sir, as well," one of them answered.

Ulrich, struck by the familiar voice, looked closer at the young man who had spoken. Then, like a thunderbolt, recognition came to him and he shouted, "Gunter! Sir, is your name Gunter?"

The young man slowly turned and faced Ulrich. "Yes, it is, sir. Have I made your acquaintance?"

"Surely you remember me, Gunter," Ulrich said.

But Ulrich, years older now and with his traditional Quaker beard, at first did not look familiar to Gunter. Ulrich smiled and greeted Gunter in German instead.

"*Ich heiße Ulrich Kessler. Guten Tag, mein Freund.*"

With that, Gunter handed his rifle to his fellow recruit, walked toward Ulrich, and threw his arms around him.

"Ulrich!" he said. "I dreamed of this day. I can't believe it's really you!"

"You are grown up now, Gunter, a fine young man. I see you are in service to your country," Ulrich said to him.

"Yes," Gunter replied. "I had been thinking of joining, and what convinced me was when Dutch came home one day and told us you'd been driven out of Germantown. It just wasn't right, and I knew it was only a matter of time before our farm was taken too. Mother didn't want me to go, but as you say, I am a grown man now. I did not wish to disrespect her wishes, but I knew I must do what was right. If we lose this war, we won't just lose our land; we'll be living forever under a tyrant, as second-class citizens. All men deserve to be free. You and Dutch taught me that."

Tears came to Ulrich's eyes, but before he could respond, Gunter added in a lighter tone, "And I told Mother not to fret, because the officer I'd talked to had told me we were going to be reinforcements at the munitions fort, guarding it against thieves. The fighting, as you know, is well to the east of us here. So we are safe for now.

"Anyway, I only have a short time today, and I see you were leaving, but I must see you again before I am sent elsewhere."

"Of course," replied Ulrich. "We have a farm east of town. Just follow the road for a couple of miles and you will come to a fork. One road has a sign reading 'To Philadelphia,' and the other will take you past my place. It is the land your grandfather deeded to me when I received my freedom. My wife's brother and I, along with our families, have made a home there. We want you to come and be our guest.

"Our place is named after my good friend," Ulrich added with a smile. "We call it *Die Deutsche Stadt*."

Gunter laughed and said, "I must see it. The next time I am off duty,

I will ride out and visit you."

"Good," replied Ulrich. "I have much to tell you, and I want you to meet my wife Anna and my family."

They looked at each other, both feeling the unspoken bond between them. Then they hugged, and each said, "Until then."

But "then" never came. A few months later, a worried Ulrich received a letter from Hans Steiner with the sad news that Gunter had been sent to the front and killed during the Battle of Princeton. Mr. Steiner had copied down for Ulrich the last letter Gunter had sent home, written only a few days before his death. Ulrich, sitting alone on his porch steps, read the words with both pride and sorrow in his heart:

MY DEAREST MOTHER,

OUR REGIMENT IS NO LONGER IN LANCASTER. A WEEK AGO, WE RECEIVED ORDERS TO JOIN COLONEL BRADFORD AND GENERAL MERCER. YESTERDAY WE FINALLY CAUGHT UP WITH GENERAL MERCER'S FORCES ON A FARM OUTSIDE OF PRINCETON. I MUST TELL YOU, THOUGH, THAT WHILE IN LANCASTER I CAME ACROSS OUR FRIEND ULRICH. HE AND HIS FAMILY MOVED THERE TWO YEARS AGO AND HAVE A FARM ON THE PROPERTY GRANDFATHER GRANTED HIM UPON HIS RELEASE. WE PLANNED TO VISIT, BUT MY REGIMENT WAS MOVED OUT THE NEXT DAY. I PLAN TO WRITE HIM AND LET HIM KNOW THAT I WILL STOP TO SEE HIM WHEN WE RETURN TO LANCASTER.

GENERAL WASHINGTON ALSO ARRIVED YESTERDAY WITH OVER SIX THOUSAND MEN. I HAVE NEVER SEEN SO MANY SOLDIERS AND

FEEL PROUD TO BE ONE OF THEM. TOMORROW MY PATROL WILL JOIN GENERAL MERCER AND A SMALL REGIMENT TO DESTROY A BRIDGE THAT THE BRITISH WILL NEED TO CROSS. WE ARE PLANNING A MAJOR ASSAULT ON THE CITY OF PRINCETON. LAST NIGHT GENERAL WASHINGTON ADDRESSED THE TROOPS AS MANY OF THEM WERE TO LEAVE ON NEW YEAR'S DAY, THEIR TIME OF DUTY BEING UP. HE APPEALED TO THEM TO STAY FOR ANOTHER SIX WEEKS AND OFFERED THEM A BOUNTY OF TEN DOLLARS TO DO SO. HE TOLD THEM THAT THEIR FREEDOM AND THE FREEDOM OF THEIR FAMILIES, THEIR WOMEN AND CHILDREN, DEPENDED ON WHAT HAPPENS ON THESE BATTLEFIELDS. THE MEN WERE TIRED, COLD, AND POORLY FED. THEY WERE BATTLE-WORN AND HUNGRY. SOME SUFFERED FROM FROSTBITE. MANY WERE WOUNDED. SOME OF THE MEN STILL LEFT AFTER HIS APPEAL, BUT MOST STAYED EVEN THOUGH THERE WERE RUMORS THAT WE WERE ALREADY SURROUNDED.

THE COURAGE I HAVE SEEN HERE IS TRULY REMARKABLE. MOTHER, IN A FEW DAYS I WILL BE GOING INTO BATTLE. I BELIEVE WHAT I AM DOING IS RIGHT. MY PRAYER IS THAT I CAN BE A MAN THAT YOU, GRANDFATHER, AND DUTCH WOULD BE PROUD OF. IF I SHOULD FALL, PLEASE KNOW THAT I DID SO DOING WHAT DUTCH AND ULRICH ALWAYS TAUGHT ME: "DO THE RIGHT THING."

GIVE MY LOVE TO MY BROTHER AND GRANDFATHER.

YOUR LOVING SON,
GUNTER

CHAPTER 38

1792: Ulrich and Daniel Leave for Kentucky

Leaving Germantown had been a difficult decision for Ulrich and Anna, but it had turned out to be the right one. Now, as Daniel and Ulrich prepared to set out for Ohio, Ulrich once again wondered if he was making the right decision in leaving Lancaster.

He and Otto had accomplished what they'd set out to do: build reputable businesses and homes together for their families and live off the twenty-five acres he had received from Mr. Steiner. It had been tough in the beginning, fighting the elements while trying to build their homes, but thanks to the other Quaker families who had already settled in Lancaster, they had gotten it done.

However, their lives in Lancaster had not been all happiness. Ulrich was saddened, thinking about the death of his two youngest children: Henry, who had died of consumption at two years of age, and an unnamed infant who had been stillborn that same year. And Anna was gone, too. The sadness had been more than she could handle, and eventually it had claimed her. She had died of a broken heart.

When Anna died, she took part of Ulrich with her. He could never truly enjoy the farm again, remembering how she had loved this land.

"The soil here is a gardener's heaven," she had often said. "It's so rich, anything would grow."

And she had proved it every spring and summer, producing more food than could be cooked or preserved. The surplus was never wasted, though, as Anna was a generous person. During the first few years of the war, the militia had become more and more dependent on the local farmers, and during harvest times, Anna would make sure a few bushel baskets were left for the men, loaded with all kinds of vegetables. Each week as the empty baskets were returned, inside was a note thanking her for her generosity, asking God to bless her. Anna kept each note folded and placed in her Bible, which she read daily.

Ulrich often wondered whether, had Anna not died, his son Abner and daughters Mary and Rebecca would still be in Lancaster. Maybe they had also been too sad, after the deaths of their mother and siblings, to remain on the land. Maybe that was one of the reasons they had both moved to Ohio, not just for the promise of a better life.

Whatever their reasons for leaving, now they were in Ohio and doing well, prospering in their new lives. Abner had married, and Mary and Rebecca both had suitors who seemed sure to propose marriage soon. Their letters all indicated that Ohio was where they wished to stay.

Only Daniel was left, and he wanted to go to Kentucky, which had just separated from Virginia and become its own state in that year of 1792. Cheap or free land was promised to anyone who would settle in this new state.

With all his children gone, there would be little left for Ulrich in Lancaster, and so he planned to go to Kentucky with Daniel, at least at first. Ulrich had not yet told Daniel that once Daniel was settled, Ulrich planned on going to Ohio to live with his other children. He hoped that by then he would have grandchildren and that he could sit on a porch swing and watch them play.

Otto had been more than fair with Ulrich in buying him out. Ulrich would have enough money to purchase a farm for Daniel if need be, to buy him some livestock, and to build him a house to get him started. What was left, the other children would receive. All the arrangements had been made, and now Daniel and Ulrich would be leaving in a couple of days.

CHAPTER 39

DANIEL AND EVE

Daniel and Ulrich traveled in a covered wagon, a small version of the Conestoga cargo wagons built in Lancaster. The wagon was pulled by two plow horses. They also had two pack mules and an extra horse that walked behind the wagon. Everything they owned was in that wagon.

They had been traveling for weeks, driving themselves hard, without stopping except to sleep at night. By the time they reached Roanoke, Virginia, it had been many days since they had seen another human being, and then it was only a trapper or two. They were running low on supplies, and they needed a break from the long, tedious journey.

So they decided to stop in Roanoke to rest and purchase supplies.

It was a decision that would change Daniel's life forever, because Eve Jefferies and her sisters were also traveling to town, to attend a church picnic on the grounds of their church, the Snow Creek Anglican Church. It was a festive occasion, and Daniel wanted to see what it was all about. The Kesslers had set up camp at a nearby stream, a branch of the James River, where they both bathed for the first time in two weeks.

Daniel put on his best shirt and trousers, trimmed his light brown hair, and mounted the riding horse. He soon arrived at the festival.

It was a beautiful autumn day in Virginia, a great day for a picnic. The children were playing games. Daniel saw young girls jumping rope and some playing London Bridge. Some of the boys were involved in a relay race where they had to balance beanbags on their heads; others were tossing horseshoes. A band was playing music, some of which Daniel recognized from his childhood: "Billy Boy," "The Patriotic Diggers," "Speed the Plough." He felt a sense of excitement as he watched the activities.

Daniel's blue eyes lit as he took notice of a striking young woman with blonde hair and fair skin. She noticed him staring, and that was enough persuasion for him to walk over to the cake table where she was working.

"Good morning, ma'am," he said. "Those sure are fine-looking cakes. How do I get one?"

"The cakes are five cents each, or we are having races later and the winners will receive a cake," she said, adding, "I haven't seen you before. Do you go to church here?"

He could not take his eyes off her.

"To be honest, my pa and I just came to town earlier today for supplies and some work. We are on our way to Kentucky."

"Would you like to take a walk around the grounds?"

"Oh, yes, ma'am," Daniel said. "I surely would."

"Now, the first thing you must do is stop calling me ma'am," said the young woman. "My name is Eve Jefferies."

"Pleased to meet you, ma'am—er—ah—Eve," he stammered. "My

name is Daniel Kessler."

"Come, Daniel. I will introduce you to my father," Eve said. "He often needs workers on the farm. Also, my uncle has a dry goods store in town and may be able to give your pa some work."

As they walked over to meet her father, Eve told Daniel about herself. "My father's large farm is outside of Roanoke, just across the James River. It is a few miles out of town, and we left just after dawn to travel to the picnic. I am the youngest of three sisters and the only one not yet married. My father always wanted sons but had three daughters instead. He never objected to my sisters getting married and leaving the farm. He is a good father and loves us all, but he needed sons."

Eventually, they were standing in front of her father.

"Father, I want you to meet Daniel Kessler," Eve said. "He is new in town. Daniel, this is my father, Rupert Jefferies."

"Hello, Daniel," Mr. Jefferies said. "I am pleased to make your acquaintance. What brings you to this part of the country?"

"My pa and I came to town for supplies and maybe to work for a while," Daniel answered. "We are on our way to Kentucky."

"It's harvest time, and I could use a couple of hands on my farm for a few weeks," Mr. Jefferies said. "I pay three guineas a week, plus three meals a day and a roof over your head. You can work until the crops are in, about three weeks from now. You will work six days a week, with Sunday as a free day."

"I will have to check with my pa, but it sounds good to me," Daniel replied. He was willing to do anything to stay close to Eve.

Daniel and Eve spent the next hour exploring the grounds. She showed him the church. Snow Creek was the oldest church in the settlement and was often used for political meetings.

The two talked and laughed and were attracted to each other. They sat on the grass and listened to the music. Their hands touched. Startled, Daniel flinched. Eve laughed and said, "Don't worry, Daniel, I won't bite." With two older, married sisters, she was more worldly than Daniel was. Their eyes met, and this time she placed her hand on his.

"I need to get back to the booth," she said. "I hope your father lets you stay and work on the farm for a while."

That night, Daniel approached his father with the idea of staying. Ulrich knew they needed a break, and the extra money for supplies would help them along their journey.

"We can stay a short time," replied Ulrich, "but I am not interested in going back to work on a farm. I will look for work in town."

CHAPTER 40

THE JEFFERIES FARM

The next morning, well before daylight, Daniel saddled his horse and left for the Jefferies farm. It was still dark when he arrived, and the men were having breakfast. Mr. Jefferies told him that he would be loading the wagons with hay. The work was hard, and by sundown his back was stiff and his hands were raw, but it was a welcome relief from long, boring days of riding in the wagon.

Eve saw him at the well, cleaning up before dinner. His shirt was unbuttoned, and she could see his lean, muscular body. She walked out to the well, and he immediately closed his shirt.

"Good evening, Miss Eve," he said. He was not sure what was proper now that he was a farmhand.

"We are friends, Daniel. You can just call me Eve," she said. "In fact, I want to invite you to come for a cup of cider on the porch tonight after you have supper with the men."

"Are you sure your father would approve?"

"I have his approval, Daniel. He knows you are different than the other men working here temporarily, that you are younger and educated, with a proper upbringing. He even told me to invite you and your father to the church service this Sunday and to join us afterward for Sunday dinner. Please tell me you will come."

That evening, after eating with the men, Daniel walked to the farmhouse, where he found Eve sitting on the porch swing. He thought she looked like an angel, sitting there in a white dress with her hair down. Daniel removed his hat when he approached her.

"Good evening, Eve. You sure do look nice tonight," he said awkwardly. He could hardly get the words out.

At her invitation, he joined her on the swing, and they talked and laughed for about an hour. Then they heard Eve's mother speak from inside the house.

"It's time to come in now, Eve," she said. "That young man needs to get his rest. He will have a long day tomorrow." The next day, Saturday, would be the day the men delivered hay to town to be sold to other farmers and to the stables.

Eve immediately stood up and asked Daniel if he could come back tomorrow.

"Yes, I would love to," he replied.

"Good. I will see you then." Then she leaned in, kissed him on the cheek, and said, "Good night, Daniel."

The next night was the same, a very pleasant evening. Daniel promised to attend church the following morning.

He and Ulrich put on their best churchgoing clothes, with coats, ties, and the like, and met the Jefferies family at the church. Afterward, the Jefferies had a big picnic set up in their yard. The food was abundant: fried chicken, beans, turnips, grits, and sweet potatoes, plus a pie and one of those cakes Daniel had admired.

It was a beautiful fall day, and it was obvious to everyone that a romance was blossoming. Ulrich couldn't help but notice, though, that the food was being prepared and served by two slave girls and one white girl he assumed was indentured. It brought back sad memories of his own childhood.

Daniel and Eve were oblivious to all this. They soon strayed away from the rest and walked through the woods and down to the stream. It was there that they first kissed. Actually, Eve initiated it. Daniel would never have had the nerve.

"Daniel, my sisters gave me this peppermint. It makes your mouth and lips sweet," she said as she looked into his eyes. She then reached up and placed a peppermint leaf into his mouth, leaned toward him, and touched her lips against his. They paused for few seconds, then embraced, and he kissed her with passion.

Soon two weeks had passed, and their courtship was in full bloom. Every day after work, he would visit her. They would walk and talk or sometimes just sit on the porch.

Ulrich was working at the dry goods store in town and still sleeping at the campsite by the river. He only saw Daniel on Sundays, when they would meet at church and sometimes have a meal together at the Jefferies farm or spend the afternoon in town. Eve always accompanied them.

At the end of the third week, Mr. Jefferies approached Daniel and said, "I can give you permanent work, Daniel, if you would like to stay."

"I would love to stay, Mr. Jefferies, but I need to finish this trip to Kentucky with my pa. It's my chance to have my own place. There are two hundred acres of prime farmland, rich in limestone, with plenty of flat land for a tobacco base and a corn crop. I appreciate your offer, but this is something I have always wanted."

That night, he told Eve about the conversation. She was upset.

"Do you mean you did not accept his offer?" she asked. "I can't believe it! I thought you loved me."

"I do love you, Eve, but this is my chance in life to make it on my own," he answered. "Come with me. We can make a life together in Kentucky. Please, Eve, tell me you will. I love you and will always take care of you. Soon the roads to Kentucky will be finished, and we will be able to travel back more easily to see your folks. Some people are traveling by boat now, which is even more comfortable. I've even heard of a new boat that is run by steam. Please, Eve, just tell me you will consider it."

"I never wanted to leave my home and family, Daniel," she said in a low voice, looking down. "But I desperately want to be with you. I accept. You will have to ask Father for permission, though, and we will have to be married before we leave."

When Daniel asked Mr. Jefferies for Eve's hand in marriage, his answer was adamant.

"It's too soon," he said. "If after Christmas you both still feel the same, then I will give you my permission."

"I will gladly wait, sir. I will do anything to prove my love for your daughter."

Even as he spoke, Daniel wondered how he would convince his father to stay so long.

But convincing Ulrich turned out not to be that difficult. He liked the job at the store, and he liked the townspeople. He also enjoyed being able to apply some of his weaving skills to making blankets for the upcoming winter. And he thought that he could be in Ohio that much sooner if Daniel decided to stay in Roanoke permanently.

BEFORE THE WEDDING

During Advent, the season before Christmas, the Anglicans of Virginia celebrated with great reverence. This was quite a change for Ulrich and Daniel, as Quakers did not regard Christmastime as any more remarkable than other times. For Anglicans, as for Catholics, Lutherans, and Moravians, Advent was a time of penance, reflection, and anticipation. The spiritual preparation was reflected most clearly in the liturgy and prayers of the church, along with daily and Sunday readings from the Book of Common Prayer. Ulrich went along with the tradition, and Daniel embraced it.

Eve and Daniel were preparing not only for Christmas but for their wedding. It was unusual to have a wedding during Advent, but the elders and Mr. Jefferies made an exception due to Daniel and Ulrich's temporary status in the town—and due to Eve's constant begging.

The wedding was an especially festive occasion. It was held on a beautiful December day, with snow on the ground and bright blue skies. There were green boughs on the church doors. Garlands of holly, ivy, mountain laurel, and mistletoe were hung from the roof, walls, pillars, and galleries. The pews, pulpit, and altar were bedecked with garlands as well. On the day of the wedding, dried lavender, rose petals, rosemary, and bay leaves were scattered throughout the church, providing a pleasant holiday scent.

But what contributed most to the ceremony was the beautiful music. The congregation sang their favorite English carols: "The Snow Lay on the Ground," "The First Noel," "God Rest Ye Merry, Gentlemen," "The Holly and the Ivy," and "I Saw Three Ships."

Yes, it was a Christmas wedding and seemed especially holy. And it was enjoyed by all, especially Eve.

A banquet followed the wedding. It consisted of onion soup, oysters on the half shell, broiled rockfish, roast suckling pig, and many, many desserts, including Christmas pudding, mince pie, eggnog, and the German, sweetened, fruit-studded bread known as stollen. It was truly a feast.

Many gifts were given that day. The one Daniel prized the most was a small box given to him by his father. He opened it to find an old army knife. Daniel looked up at his father with a puzzled expression on his face.

"This is the knife your grandfather gave to me the day I was taken from him," Ulrich said, with a smile but with sadness in his eyes. "Now I want it to be yours."

It was a happy time for all, although Mr. Jefferies still had mixed emotions about Eve going to Kentucky. He knew of the Wilderness Trail they would have to travel. He still had hopes that they would decide to stay in Roanoke; he had one more idea that might just work. He knew that they would not be allowed to leave during the Christmas season, and then winter would set in, with plenty of time to convince them to stay.

His wife reminded him of how, when he was a young man, he had left his family in Connecticut to travel to Virginia to buy land.

"Nothing could have kept you from getting your own land," she reminded him, "and you are where you are today because of that ambition. You were younger than Daniel then, and I was younger than Eve. They are young and in love and must find their own way in life, take their own chances, experience their own successes and failures. Let them go, dear; they are under enough pressure. My heart will break when Eve leaves, but I know she is happy with Daniel, and he will take care of her. If after the Christmas season they still want to go, Rupert, I beg you not to interfere."

Mr. Jefferies just stood looking at her, not giving the slightest hint of whether she was getting through to him, whether he would ever let them go.

Christmas came and went, and still Mr. Jefferies refused to give his blessings. And there were celebrations for weeks after Christmas: for the circumcision of Jesus on January 1, Epiphany on January 6, the Purification of the Virgin on February 2. Then Mr. Jefferies told Daniel and Eve, "You could never get across that trail in this ice and cold. It is simply too treacherous. I won't allow it."

But Daniel knew that some actually preferred to travel in the winter, when the rivers were frozen for easier crossing. And he knew Ulrich was becoming impatient too. Ulrich would soon make the decision for everyone.

CHAPTER 42

THE WILDERNESS TRAIL

In early February of 1793, Ulrich told Daniel they would need to leave before the end of the month.

"We need to go before the melting of the snow in the mountains," he said. "The rivers and streams will be too swollen after that."

Eve was extremely happy living in Roanoke on her father's farm. He had provided to her and Daniel their own love nest, a cabin with wood floors, windows, and a fireplace. So Daniel avoided telling her for as long as he could, considering that there needed to be preparation for the long, hard, and dangerous journey.

Unlike the Great Philadelphia Wagon Road, which Ulrich and Daniel had followed from Lancaster to Roanoke, the Wilderness Road, which would take them through the Cumberland Gap into Kentucky, was impassable in a wagon. They would be crossing the Allegheny Mountains on foot and on horseback, usually single file over rocky dirt paths created over hundreds of years by woodland buffalo, deer, and elk and later by Cherokee and Shawnee Indians. The route was dangerous and exhausting as it wound its way through a maze of narrow-ridged mountains and steep-sided valleys, across swollen rivers that, even before the spring thaw, were hazardous to cross. Rains also could cause flash floods, making the narrow paths even more treacherous.

When Daniel did tell Eve it was time to go, she was upset, but they both knew she had no choice. They began preparing for the journey. Ulrich sold his wagon and the plow horses and bought three saddle horses, one for each of them, plus two pack mules and an extra horse. He also bought nonperishable supplies such as flour, coffee, and dried peas. Ulrich and Daniel were confident that with the abundant game of deer, buffalo, elk, turkey, and pheasant along the trail, along with smaller game like rabbit and squirrel, there would be plenty of meat. Fruit and nuts, mostly walnuts and hazelnuts, would also be plentiful, and fresh water and fish would be in abundance in the rivers and creeks they would cross.

They left early in the morning on February 28, 1793. The weather was still cold, but with campfires and blankets, the Kesslers would be fairly comfortable. By most standards, they were wealthy travelers. Each had their own mount, and they had plenty of food, guns, and ammunition for the long trip. They also had provisions such as hemp canvases, which Ulrich had woven to serve as protection at night against the rains.

The first few days of the trip were uneventful, with Ulrich leading the way. The two pack mules followed them, then Eve on her horse, then Daniel in the rear with the extra horse. Each day, they would pitch camp at dusk, build a fire, and retire early. Often Ulrich would get up before dawn to kill a rabbit or squirrel for breakfast, and Eve, who was handy with a skillet, would make biscuits or corn cakes. The streams were still mostly frozen, but they were thawed enough for Daniel to get drinking water, which meant hot coffee in the mornings.

They had not seen another human for four days when one morning, about dawn, Ulrich was scouting the woods around them and saw an Indian boy about thirteen years old. Evidently the boy was also scouting and hunting; at least Ulrich hoped so. The French and Indian War was over, and most of the Indian tribes were now peaceful, but Ulrich and Daniel had been warned about renegades roaming the hills, stealing horses and supplies. There had also been a massacre in 1786 along the route, where a family of twenty had been killed by Indians.

For these reasons, Ulrich was suspicious and cautious concerning the Indians. However, the boy just stared for a few moments and then turned and disappeared into the woods.

Many people had told Ulrich that he should try to meet up with other travelers, that there was safety in numbers. It worried him that the Indian boy had seen him; he was sure the Kesslers' presence would be reported to others, possibly to the same young renegades who caused trouble.

Ulrich had been told that he would most likely find other travelers at a river, where many stopped for a day to rest, bathe, and spell the animals. He decided to stop at a small river just ahead.

Though he saw no other travelers when his party arrived at the river's edge, he decided to wait to see whether others would join them. The fishing was good, and Daniel and Eve were enjoying rest, delicious meals of fresh trout, campfires at night, and time together. Eve especially enjoyed the opportunity to bathe. Daniel would heat water over the fire for her and provide privacy with a canvas.

On the third day, a group from Tennessee came down the trail. After a welcome by Ulrich and a friendly greeting from the newcomers, all set up camp and decided to sup together. As supper was prepared, the travelers shared their stories.

Boyd McGregor was thirty-five. His parents had migrated to America from Scotland after the Battle of Culloden in April of 1746. With his parents both gone now, he had decided to give up sharecropping and sheep herding and move his family to Kentucky, where land was plentiful. He wanted to have his own sheep ranch and provide wool for the weavers and textile mills. He was traveling with his wife Aileen and their three children, daughters Senga and Beatrice and young son Lindsey. Aileen was visibly pregnant, but Boyd said they should be across the gap into Kentucky before she was due to deliver.

With the McGregors was a young couple, Kerr and Catrina Kilpatrick, also Scottish immigrants. They had met the McGregors on the trail.

Each of the Kilpatricks had mounts, and they had a pack horse, but the McGregors only had two horses between them, with one being used for supplies. The McGregors were taking turns walking and riding; a lot of the trail had to be made on foot anyway. And the Kilpatricks had been willing to have the children ride pillion on their own horses.

Ulrich was glad to see the newcomers and hoped they would travel with him, Daniel, and Eve. He was especially glad to see they were well armed.

As the travelers gathered for supper around the fire, they knew rough times were ahead, but that night they were at peace and prayed together over their meal of fresh trout, rabbit, and a pheasant Ulrich had shot that morning. After the meal, Boyd opened a jug and poured the men a cup of Irish whiskey. All was well on the frontier.

It was not to last, though. The next morning before daylight, Daniel was awakened by the neighing and snorting of the horses. Looking up, he saw two young Indian boys untying a few of the horses. He immediately grabbed his rifle and fired a warning shot into the air. It was too late, though; the boys jumped onto one of the horses and rode off into the woods, and Daniel saw a few other boys running alongside them. By then, the other men were up and armed. The men saddled up and chased the boys, but they were long gone.

No one was hurt, but the Kessler family was down one horse. They would have to take turns riding, which would make the trip even more difficult.

CHAPTER 43

HOME

The traveling parties stayed by the river for several days, and the four men took turns guarding the camp during the night. After crossing the river, they continued through the gap that crossed the Alleghenies, a path so treacherous that travelers called it the "Devil's Stairway." The trail was riddled with both marked and unmarked graves from parties of settlers who had pushed through, leaving their dead behind, determined to find a place they and their families could live and thrive.

Though the Kessler party did not encounter any more Indians along the trail, they knew that bands of Shawnee still roamed the area, and as they got closer to Fort Boonesborough, they came across a settlement with graves of more than twenty victims of an Indian massacre, mainly from one family, the McNitts.

When they reached Fort Boonesborough, all stopped to rest, wash, and resupply. Like many families, the McGregors decided to stay in the area. They liked the landscape of hills and valleys with streams; it reminded them of Scotland. It would be a good place for raising sheep. Daniel, like many other pioneers, thought any place with people living closer than five miles apart was too crowded. So the Kesslers, along with the Kilpatricks and two other young couples they met at the fort, kept moving.

Daniel was determined to reach Green County in south central Kentucky. He had seen notices that in this new county, land was being offered for as little as thirty dollars for one hundred acres. In fact, he had such a notice in his pocket. Daniel would have enough money to buy two hundred acres, with enough left over to buy livestock and build a cabin and barn.

When they arrived in Green County, they set up camp a few miles southwest of the new county seat, Greensburg. Then Daniel traveled to the land grant office in town to file his claim. He soon realized the land grant office was the most popular place in town. People from all over were coming there for the opportunity to own a farm.

Daniel finally got in to see the clerk in charge and showed him the notice that he had been carrying for almost two years. The clerk smiled.

"Do you know how many of these I've seen?" he asked. "Doesn't mean anything yet, young man. The land grant hasn't passed. The only thing you can do now is pick out the land you desire, and for a twenty-five-dollar deposit, you can have first choice if the land grant passes."

"But I need to be settled," said Daniel. "My wife and father and I have been traveling for months. The notice says the land is available now."

"Sorry, son. There are lots of folks here in the same and even worse shape than you. If you have the twenty-five dollars, my suggestion would be to pick you out a plot of land from that map over on the wall and put the deposit down. Then you can go ahead and settle on the land. It will be yours if the grant passes; if not, you will get your money back, but the land won't belong to you, and you may have to move on with nothing to show for your work. It's your choice. I wouldn't tarry too long, though; the plots are going fast."

Daniel saw on the map that there was a two-hundred-acre plot of land across the county line in Adair County, close to where they had set up camp. It was called Sulphur Creek after the waterway that bordered the land. The downside was that the plot was almost half-covered with woods, but that still left over one hundred acres of good farmland, and the trees would provide plenty of lumber to build a house and barn as well as providing firewood for the winter. The creek would also provide plenty of water for the livestock and crops and an endless supply of fresh fish.

That afternoon, Daniel and Ulrich rode out to the land and surveyed it as best they could. Daniel was excited and saw nothing but opportunity and independence. Ulrich, on the other hand, saw nothing but backbreaking work and fighting the elements for a successful crop. He wanted no part of it. His days of milking at dawn and stripping tobacco until dusk were over.

"We can always go on to Ohio and join the rest of the family, Daniel," he said. "I could teach you the weaving trade, or you could find other work in the town."

Daniel looked at his father in puzzlement.

"This is my home now, Pa," he said. "I will build my life here and raise a family. I will have the farm I always dreamed of. I hope you will stay. We will build you a place of your own. Surely there will be opportunity here for you."

Ulrich answered simply, "Daniel, one day I will be going to Ohio."

Even though there was no guarantee that the grant would pass, Daniel decided to put the money down and proceed. It was now March, and he knew the ground needed to be prepared for planting in April. It would only be on a limited basis this first year. But at least they could start a garden to provide them with vegetables, and they could depend on hunting and fishing for meat. Ulrich was able to find some odd jobs around the new settlement, which provided money to buy staples. Fortunately, it was spring and the weather was good, so the tents and lean-to they put up were adequate shelter, even though the nights could sometimes be cool.

There were other families along the creek who were in the same situation. Some had even started to clear land, but Daniel was reluctant to do so until the land grant was approved and he owned the property. However, around the first week of May, Eve told him that she was with child, and he decided to get started. He bought a two-man saw and two axes, and early one morning he and Ulrich walked to the woods to cut down their first tree. Ulrich was an expert with an ax due to all the wood he'd cut for Dutch at the cabin. So the first tree fell, and their mission to build a home and barn had begun. Eve watched with tears in her eyes but joy in her heart. As she told Daniel, she felt she was finally home.

Soon they had dug a foundation for the house and had many logs cut. But before they could start building, a gentleman who almost looked like a preacher, all dressed in black and wearing a hat with a red band, rode out to the camp. He was met by Ulrich.

"Hello, sir," called Ulrich. "How can I help you?"

The man replied with a big smile, "It is I who can help *you*, sir. Is your name Daniel Kessler?"

"No, but I am Daniel's father," said Ulrich.

Eve walked up and asked Ulrich, "What is it, Ulrich? Is something wrong?"

"And this is Daniel's wife, Mrs. Kessler," Ulrich said to the man.

"Pleased to make your acquaintance, ma'am," said the man. "My name is Charles Toups, and I am a surveyor with the land grant company. I bring you good news. The land grant has been approved. Soon the land will be officially yours, if you and your husband still want it. But my company is willing to buy it back from you if you have changed your mind."

Eve did not answer but turned and hugged Ulrich and then ran toward the wood where Daniel was working, shouting behind her as she ran.

"We want to keep the land, Mr. Toups!"

"Wait!" he shouted. "You have to come to town, sign more papers, and either pay the rest of the cash or take out a note!"

Ulrich assured him that they would be there tomorrow to pay off the remainder of the note and claim their deed.

"Daniel, Daniel, I have good news," Eve shouted as she ran toward her husband. When she got to him, she jumped into his arms, hugging his neck and wrapping her legs around his waist. Then she kissed him.

"What is it, Eve? I haven't seen you this excited since our wedding."

"Oh, Daniel, it's ours! The land grant was approved. This is our home!"

And both of them fell to their knees and wept, still embracing, Eve tearfully giving thanks to the Lord.

CHAPTER 44

ULRICH LEAVES FOR OHIO

The first year on the farm was difficult for the Kessler family. Most of their money had been spent on the land, and little was left for tools, livestock, and building supplies. Ulrich and Daniel continued to cut logs for the cabin and barn, but it was a slow process, especially since Ulrich was still working odd jobs in town to buy needed supplies.

Daniel was able to put in a productive garden that supplied them with fresh vegetables, tomatoes, green beans, corn, lettuce, peppers, turnips, potatoes, even watermelon. There were apple trees in the forest and plenty of blackberries to pick. Eve even put in an herb garden and tended to a robust strawberry patch. Daniel set trot lines in Sulphur Creek, which supplied plenty of catfish. Ulrich still liked to hunt and trap, but he stayed with small game, because the family had no way of keeping meat fresh. He was also able to earn a little extra money by trapping and selling the furs. More people were moving into the area, and the fur trade was booming.

So the Kesslers were surviving, but by September of that first year on Sulphur Creek, the house and barn were not yet built. Discouragement was setting in, especially for Eve, who was well into her seventh month of pregnancy and still living in a tent.

Then a strange series of coincidences happened.

Ulrich was made aware of a group of Quakers who had traveled to the area and were camping on Sulphur Creek on their way to Fort Harrod. He heard about a service they were having and decided to attend. This did not sit well with many of the other settlers in Green County, who were mostly mainstream Protestants. One of the reasons they opposed the Quakers was the fact that most Quakers opposed slavery and some even worked as part of the Underground Railroad, helping enslaved people to escape. In the slaveholding society that was Kentucky at the time, such beliefs and activities were frowned upon.

The local opposition did not deter Ulrich from attending the service. It was a simple service, with men, women, and children standing in silence, waiting expectantly to come into the presence of the Divine and to be guided by the still, small voice by which God might speak to them from within. During the silence, anyone—man, woman, or child—might feel moved to offer a simple spoken message inspired by this holy encounter. This was a regular Quaker practice, and Ulrich was used to it. But in this service, people from time to time during an "inspired message" would start shaking, and some would break out into an energetic dance. This was very strange to him.

After the service, Ulrich was approached by a few men who welcomed him to their community. Ulrich told them that he had become a Quaker and attended meetings on a regular basis in Pennsylvania, but he had never experienced the dancing and shaking he had seen that night.

The men explained to him that they were Quakers, and as such, they were pacifists who believed that God is in every person. But they were of a special sect that was also devoted to Spiritualism, to the equality of men and women, and to celibacy. While the Shakers welcomed and raised children, all the children were either from their lives before becoming Shakers or had been adopted into the group.

"Our belief in celibacy is the key feature that distinguishes us from the Quakers, who sometimes refer to us as the Shaking Quakers," said one man. "Because of this nickname, we have come to call ourselves Shakers."

He bid Ulrich goodbye, inviting him back to another service the following night. Again, Ulrich went to the service; again, there was plenty of shaking. To his surprise, though, he saw a familiar face: a good friend from Germantown, Friedrich Hess.

After the service, he approached him.

"Friedrich Hess, is it really you?"

Friedrich turned toward the voice and, in disbelief, threw up his hands and exclaimed, "Ulrich, I can't believe it is you, here in this place."

They hugged, and after a period of courtesies, they asked after each other's families. Friedrich then invited Ulrich to sit and eat with the group. As the evening progressed, Ulrich told about his travels with Daniel and Eve and about the situation they were in now, still living in tents after several months. He also mentioned Eve's pregnancy. Friedrich, in turn, explained that the Shakers in his party had come from Pennsylvania and were waiting for another group to join them; then all would travel to Fort Harrod to establish a Shaker village there. He had traveled this far with the new group, but as he did not accept their belief in celibacy, he would not be going on to Fort Harrod with them.

The next morning at daybreak, Ulrich was sitting by the fire having a cup of coffee. For the moment, he was alone; Daniel was already in the field, and Eve was preparing breakfast. Then Ulrich saw images heading his way in the light fog. At first, he was alarmed and grabbed his rifle. But as the images became clearer, he could see several horse- and ox-drawn wagons. And then he saw his friend Friedrich.

It was the men of the Shaker community. Their wagons were full of tools. They had come to build a home for the Kessler family.

"We will only be in this place for a short time," said one of the elders, "but while we are here, we want to do the work of God and help our fellow man. We will build your home for you."

With that, they began to work with unbelievable precision and organization. It was like being in the presence of thirty or forty Ottos; all were expert at what they did. Working in teams the first day, some went to the forest to cut trees, while others set up a temporary sawmill where the logs were turned into lumber—rough lumber, but still lumber. Some cleared the land where the barn would go. The barn was the main structure, for without it, no farm could survive.

After the cutting of the lumber and the preparation of the worksite, it only took one day to "raise" the barn. It was a routine obviously performed many times before. The house was another story. It took fewer men but several days to finish it. But when it was done, Daniel and Eve finally had a home. Though small and relatively primitive, it was strongly built. It consisted of a living area that had a fireplace and a cookstove, one bedroom for Daniel and Eve, and a loft for the children who were to come.

The Shaker men even built a new outhouse to replace the makeshift outhouse Daniel and Ulrich had quickly put together when they'd arrived.

To prepare the house for Daniel and Eve, Ulrich had sold a few of his furs and bartered work in exchange for pillows and a feathered mattress. They already had plenty of blankets, but some of the Quaker women also gave them quilts, along with a crib that had been made, they said sadly, for a baby who had died.

The mother cried when giving the crib to Eve but said, "A crib is for a baby, not for a memory."

It took several days for the Shakers, Ulrich, and Daniel to finish the work together. On the last day, when the work was done, the house and barn were dedicated with a service of gratitude followed by a celebratory meal. Ulrich and Daniel had killed a large buck, and it had been roasting over an open pit until time to eat; Eve and the Shaker women had prepared breads and vegetables. In typical Quaker fashion, the group formed a circle and held hands in silence as each of them in their own way gave thanks and said grace in private. Before the "amen" and the breaking of the circle, Friedrich offered a prayer for the Kessler family and for their new baby who would soon arrive.

As they feasted, Friedrich asked Ulrich, "Where will you be living, now that Daniel has a home? Are you going to be staying in their cabin?"

"No, I am not settling here," Ulrich replied. "I will be leaving for Ohio to join my daughter and other family members in Montgomery County. I plan to settle there, live in town, and resume my weaving trade." Then he added with a big smile, "My farming days will soon be over for good."

"That is very interesting, Ulrich," Friedrich said, "because I also am going on to Ohio just as soon as my brother and his group arrive here from New Jersey. Perhaps you would like to travel with us. We plan to go north to Jefferson County, cross the Ohio River by flatboat, then make our way northeast. We could all travel together until we reach where your family lives, and then my family and I will go on to our destination."

Ulrich gladly accepted, and the next day, he told Daniel of his plan. Daniel was upset, but he had known this day would come.

"Pa, we have been over this many times," Daniel said. "You know I want you to stay, but most of all, I want you to be happy. I know you have not been that happy here, and I appreciate all you have done for Eve and me. Will you at least stay until after the baby is born?"

"Of course," Ulrich replied. "We will not be leaving until spring anyway; by the time Friedrich's family arrives, it will be too late to travel until next spring."

In November, little Sarah was born in Daniel and Eve's new home, with the aid of a midwife who had delivered many babies. The following spring, after the rainy season, when the weather was dry and the rivers were down, Friedrich and Ulrich began making plans for their departure. By this time, Friedrich's brother and his family had been in Kentucky for a month and they were all anxious to get started, as was Ulrich.

So on the third of April, 1794, Ulrich headed out with the Hess family to his new home in Ohio. Even though he vowed to return for a visit, this was his last journey; Daniel never saw him again.

PART THREE

CHAPTER 45

DARDY

By 1819, many desperate families were traveling the Wilderness Trace, heading west, searching for a new life. Kentucky had been the fifteenth state in the union since 1792, but land was still plentiful there at a very low price; some was even free.

Gerhardt Sadler was a farmer without a farm. He was determined to find land west of the Alleghenies. He decided to take his family west out of Virginia, despite the warnings by locals of Cherokee uprisings. Although by now many Cherokees had moved farther west, bands of renegades and small tribes that wanted to stay in the area roamed the Wilderness Trail, and some were exacting violent revenge on the white settlers who had displaced and abused their people.

Sadler, his wife Ona, their twin sons Alexander and Augustus, and their daughter Dorothy, whom they called Dardy, planned to meet up with other families and travel west together; there was safety in numbers.

Alexander and Augustus were fourteen. Like their father, they were large, strong boys and handy with their rifles. Dardy was sixteen, and she had been nothing but trouble to her parents since she'd reached puberty. Though she could read and write due to her mother's training when she was a young girl, she'd had little more opportunity for schooling, and her boredom and restlessness expressed themselves in her actions. She was already known in the Roanoke area as a girl of loose morals who liked to abide with liquor and the boys.

Dardy did not want to go on this trip. Her father had to threatened to tie her to the wagon if she kept refusing to go.

Like many families, the Sadlers left Virginia in the early spring, as soon as the winter ice began to melt. As always, the gap presented dangerous situations, but once they were through the gap, the trace became much easier to travel. On occasion they ran across other settlers, but not the caravan they were looking for. Soon, though, they were only a few miles from the meeting place where they would join other travelers. Gerhardt knew that once they hooked up with the caravan, travel would be much safer. However, they decided to stop that evening and join the others the next day.

As they sat by the fire, three white men on horses approached the camp. Gerhardt offered them coffee, which they accepted. At first they seemed friendly enough, but it soon became obvious that was not the case.

"You should be on your way now," Gerhardt said. "The others will be joining us soon." Of course, he knew there were no "others" coming.

Sensing their father's concern, Alexander and Augustus stood with their rifles in their arms.

The three strangers sized up the situation. They knew there were money, supplies, and horses for the taking, and they especially liked the idea of taking the women captive, for various reasons. However, with the two boys already standing with rifles, now would not be a good time to rob them. Leaving was the better option.

Later, in the dark of night, a shot rang out. The three men had returned and surrounded the Sadlers' camp. Augustus, who was standing watch, was hit in the throat. Blood spurted out profusely. As he reached for the wound in his throat, another bullet struck him in the back, and he fell to the ground helpless and dying. Gerhardt and Alexander had sprung to their feet with rifles in hand, but they also fell to the ground, riddled with bullets.

Now only the two Sadler women were left alive. Ona ran to secure guns, but she was soon wrestled to the ground by one of the men. Then she and Dardy were tied up and placed on horses, and the men rode off with them.

"Why are we taking them with us?" one of the men asked. "We have their money and horses. Let's just have a little fun with the women and then let them go. Once the Cherokee renegades get them, they will wish they were dead like their men."

"We will use them to bargain with the Indians for safe passage," said another man, obviously the group's leader. "They were a big reason for us doing what we did. The Indians treasure white women captives. But don't you worry none, they will be with us for a few days. It will be kind of nice having something to poke besides them whores around the station camps."

For the next few days, the men traveled toward Hazel Patch, a fort and settlement at the crossroads of the trail. By day, they treated Ona and Dardy fairly well, sharing food and water with them, allowing them to bathe and wash what clothes they needed and dry them by the evening campfires. But that wasn't because the ruffians cared about the women. They only wanted them to look good, to be good bargaining chips with the Indians. By night, the men took turns raping both mother and daughter.

On the fifth day, they came across a small band of Cherokees who seemed interested in the women. The Indians were led by a young man who spoke a little English. It didn't matter, though; one of the white men could speak enough Cherokee to get by. The white men told the Indians that they were helping the women, whom they'd found traveling alone after their husband and father had been killed by a bear. The leader of the ruffians told the Indians they did not want to keep the women with them, slowing them down. They offered the Cherokees the women and a horse in return for safe passage.

The three Indian men said they would have to get approval from their leaders and would return. Soon they did return, in full battle attire and war paint . . . but not to bargain.

The attack was swift and brutal. Two of Ona and Dardy's captors were wounded with arrows immediately. The third took off on his horse. For a wild moment, Dardy hoped he would escape, so that he could tell the story; she hoped that if white people knew where she and her mother were, someone would come to their rescue. It could be their only hope of getting away from the Indians.

It wasn't to be, though. The third man was soon overtaken and was beaten and scalped by the Indians. They removed from him what clothes and weapons they wanted and left him, knowing he would freeze to death if he were lucky and be eaten by wolves or other wild animals if he weren't. The other two captors, badly wounded, were dragged back to the camp and spread-eagled on the ground. Their shirts and boots were removed and were tied to stakes outside the camp, left to be eaten by animals. The women were bound and placed on the ground.

Little did the men know that the small band of Indians had come upon the massacre of the Sadler men. By then, white families were generally being allowed to pass through Cherokee land as long as they didn't hunt, steal, or settle there. Only small bands of Cherokees were still fighting the settlers, and this band wasn't among them. But the killers had made several mistakes with the Cherokee. The men had lied to the Indians about the women and how they came to have them. But even more damning were the pelts hanging from their horses, along with Indian moccasins and feathers from a type of headgear usually worn by Indian boys.

The men, Ona, and Dardy survived the night. The next day, the Indians returned, untied the women, and walked them a short distance away to where the Indians had set up camp. Some Indians stayed there to watch the women, and some returned and stripped the men of the rest of their clothes. Honey was spread over the white men's torsos; soon they would be covered by fire ants. By that night, the men were swollen and had red bites all over them, but things only got worse. The Indians built small fires at the tips of their fingers and the soles of their feet, roasting them slowly.

Their screams were heard by the women during the night. Ona wanted to go and kill them somehow, to put them out of their misery, but Dardy stopped her.

"They killed our whole family," she reminded her mother fiercely.

Ona abided by Dardy's insistence. The men died early the next day and were left to rot.

Ona and Dardy were treated well by the Indians. They were given Indian food: deer, buffalo meat, and fish. Three days after the white men died, Ona and Dardy were put on horses, and the Indian party traveled for a whole day. That night, the women were tied up and slept in the open with the men, one blanket for each person. The men did not bother them, even though Dardy had already started acting in a flirty manner.

The next day they arrived at a large encampment of houses made of woven saplings, plastered with mud, and roofed with poplar bark. There were women and children there, along with more men. Ona and Dardy were taken to the chief; he would decide their fate.

He told the others in the council, "The white soldiers will soon come looking for them. We do not want more war with the 'bluecoats.' The women may remain with us until it is a good time to take them back to their own people. They can leave at any time, but at their own peril. We will not escort them."

The women were then taken to an area primarily of other women and children and shown the hut where they would eat and sleep.

As time went on, Dardy adjusted to her new life, but Ona was sick and could hardly eat. She was heartbroken over losing her husband and two sons. She felt hopeless and had very little fight left in her. Growing thinner and weaker by the day, Ona hardly ever left the hut and the immediate area around it. She had no desire to adjust to the Indian way of life; she longed to be back in Virginia. The Cherokee women were kind to her and tried to soothe her with herbs and ointments, but she continued to waste away.

One day, when Ona was feverish and weak and appeared to be dying, a medicine woman came and, without asking Ona or Dardy, built a small fire in the hut. She was accompanied by a young girl of the tribe.

The medicine woman's name was Hummingbird Blossom. She was held in high esteem in the tribe and in the Cherokee nation. More than most other Indian tribes, the Cherokee considered their women as equals to men. Men and women had different roles, but they were both valued. Some women were able to serve on leadership councils and even war councils.

As in numerous other Indian tribes, the Cherokees' knowledge of medicine was handed down from generation to generation through those who were considered to be "chosen" as healers. Hummingbird Blossom, who was in her eighties, was one of those chosen, and her mother and grandmother had taught her well.

As she sat by the fire, she smoked a pipe, squinting against the smoke, which accentuated the fact that her creased eyes looked almost closed. Her skin was wrinkled and leathery, and it sagged as if it had melted over the years.

Soon, with the help of the young Indian girl, Hummingbird knelt down beside Ona and directed the smoke over her. She instructed the girl to put dried feverwort and bark from dogwood and willow trees into a pot of water that she had set to heat on the small fire. She started a chant that continued for several minutes while she moved an eagle feather over Ona's body. She blew smoke over Ona. Then she instructed the young girl to give the "tea" from the pot to Ona.

The tea did seem to help Ona, and she fell asleep while Hummingbird was still with her.

Ona died about three months later. Hummingbird had not been able to save her, but she had made the end easier. Ona had suffered from headaches, and the tea Hummingbird made from pennyroyal had seemed to ease the pain. In the end, though, her broken heart and broken spirit took her life.

The Cherokee are a very spiritual people, viewing death as a transition rather than an end. Ona's body was prepared by first washing it, then bathing it with scented oils. The belief was that the oils had a strong spiritual property for cleansing impurities. Her body was wrapped in a blanket made of grasses and herbs and placed into the ground to nourish the earth, with an eagle feather placed on the body. The Cherokee venerate the eagle as a sacred bird.

The funeral began with prayers by a shaman; the body was then carried to its final resting place. For Ona, this was outside the Cherokee burial grounds. Dardy had one of the young men bring her a small flat rock to be used as a headstone. She laid it flat on the ground above Ona's head. On it, she used Indian paint to write, "Ona Sadler, Wife and Mother, 1778–1819." Ona had died at only forty-one years of age.

Dardy was sad and cried at the funeral, even though crying did not come easily for her. She had loved her mother and would miss her. But she vowed that she would survive, no matter what she had to do.

CHAPTER 46

GALEGENOH

As time went on, the self-centered Dardy adjusted to her new life, as she had vowed to do. She was going to take care of herself.

A few weeks after Ona died, Dardy decided to put away her frontierswoman's clothes and start dressing in Indian garb. Soon, she was getting plenty of attention in her deerskin dress, which only came to her knees, though a fringe at the bottom added another four inches to the length. She enjoyed the attention she was getting from a few of the young men. The women warned her to stay away from them, but she was a creature who loved excitement and had already been sexual back in Virginia.

She became very flirty with the boys, and on one occasion she went off into the woods with them, where they drank alcohol together. Not being used to it, she became very drunk, and before the night was over, all three of the young men had their way with her. They then nicknamed her "Spantsa," which means "unquenchable lust" or, in some tribes, "rotten womb."

Things eventually settled down, and Dardy was becoming more and more accepted by the tribe. The three boys from the drinking session were already spoken for by Indian girls, and after that day in the woods, they avoided Dardy as much as possible. She was at peace with her situation but lonely; she missed her family and the sense of belonging.

Just over a month after the incident in the woods, which most of the tribe had heard about but had assumed was just bragging by the boys, Dardy first laid eyes on Galegenoh. He and some other young men were returning to the camp after a long hunting trip. Behind him were two pack horses pulling a cart full of the kill from the hunt.

Galegenoh was wearing a beige cotton shirt, probably taken from white men in exchange for passage; it was open in the front. He was wearing a loincloth and leggings which did little to hide his long, muscular legs. His moccasins were sewn in front, and around his waist was a beaded belt. He still carried a bow and a large supply of arrows across his back, even though he had a rifle in a sleeve on his horse. On one side of his waist hung a knife and on the other side a tomahawk. His face was lean, with high cheekbones and black eyebrows and hair. His chest was smooth and bare except for a small necklace made of pieces of stag antlers. Two feathers dangled from the crown of his head, and the rims of his ears were pierced many times with small objects. Later, Dardy would learn that each earring represented something significant in his life. Galegenoh's first wife had been murdered by white trappers, and three of the earrings on the rim of his ear represented scalps taken from those who had raped and killed his wife.

He was at least ten years older than Dardy, but she immediately wanted to know more about this magnificent specimen of a man and she soon would.

The women of the tribe began collecting the meat from the cart. They would start preparing it right away. Everything on the animal would be used. What they could not eat would be made into weapons and warm clothing.

Dardy walked toward Galegenoh and stared up at him. She said nothing. He looked down at her and also said nothing, but he felt an attraction and familiarity. It was only when she got close enough to his horse and saw the initials carved on the stock of the rifle that she realized why he seemed familiar. The initials were G. S., for Gerhardt Sadler. Galegenoh had led the war party that had rescued her and her mother.

That night there was to be a great celebration for the success of the hunt, for now the tribe was set to survive the winter with plenty of meat, grease, fur, and leather. The fires were built. The men danced around one and the women around another. Most of the men were drinking. As the night went on, the dancing became intense, and the dancers became more intoxicated by dance and by whiskey. The combination served as an aphrodisiac, and many of the men left to find their wives and retire to their huts for a night of passion. Other couples sneaked off into the woods.

Galegenoh was one of the last men to leave the dance. He noticed Dardy standing and watching the women go through their gyrations. She had not learned the dance moves yet, but she was captivated by the drums, the fire, and the shadows of bodies moving in the dark with only the fire and the moon providing light.

As Galegenoh walked toward her, he was taken aback by her beauty: her skin glistening in the flames of the fire, her hair pulled back with a band around the back which also held one white feather. She was wearing a leather mantle with fringe in the front and a skirt woven of mulberry bark. Her eyes, accentuated by turquoise earrings dangling from her earlobes, sparkled as they reflected the flickering flames.

She felt his presence. She looked up to see him staring at her. She quickly looked down.

"Why are you not dancing?" he asked as he neared her.

"I am a white girl," she said. "Besides, I have never mastered the dances and their meanings."

"This is a celebration dance," he said. "We are giving thanks to the Great Spirit for the bountiful hunt."

He then asked her if she would walk with him, as he was growing weary of the dance. She agreed to do so, not realizing that an acceptance meant more than just walking. They walked to the edge of the camp, where a stream reflected the full moon.

There was no foreplay, not even kissing. Galegenoh simply spread his blanket down and motioned for Dardy to lie on it. She realized now what being asked for a "walk" actually meant. She obeyed his gesture, and soon he was on top of her, pushing the soft mulberry skirt up. Like most Cherokee women, she wore nothing underneath.

After making love, they stayed under the moonlight for a long time. They did not say much, but Dardy felt a closeness that she had never known with a man before, and it had been a long time for Galegenoh.

"You will be my woman now, when the time is right," Galegenoh said. "I will tell the chief."

Dardy knew not to object. It was the Indian way, and he was an older, respected man who could be chief someday. She knew in time she would have to share him with a Cherokee woman—he would want children of pure Cherokee blood—but for now, she would have him to herself.

He gave her an Indian name, AhWeeNee, which meant "fawn," and he marked her face with a tattoo of stag antlers on her left cheek; the name Galegenoh meant "stag." This tattoo would mark Dardy for life, but she was happy to have Galegenoh as her man. He would protect and care for her.

Life went on like this for three years. Every year, Galegenoh would leave with many of the other men to hunt buffalo.

It was during one of these trips that Dardy's life changed dramatically.

CHAPTER 47

DARDY LEAVES THE TRIBE

One day in the early spring of 1822, a band of long hunters, white men who made their living hunting through the Appalachian woods, rode into camp. They knew it would be safer to approach the camp at this time, during the buffalo hunt, when many of the young men were away. They brought pelts as a peace offering in return for safe passage, though by then most of the Cherokees who would attack whites had moved west toward Fort Harrod and Fort Boonesborough.

The three long hunters had only been in camp a short time when one of them, Seth Thomas, spotted the "white girl." They had heard this tribe had two white women, but they'd had no idea one of the women was actually a beautiful young girl. Dardy, seeing Seth's stare, looked at him defiantly, but he was already making plans to leave with her.

Seth was dressed in skins from animals he had killed. He wore a hat made from fox fur that covered most of his forehead, almost to his dark eyebrows. His dark beard accentuated his good looks and large, solid frame.

Seth was a decent man but very rugged. He considered women a liability for the most part, but he missed their companionship.

The next day when he met with the chief, he bartered for Dardy with pelts, tobacco, a horse, and whiskey. The wise old chief also wanted Seth's pipe, which he smoked continuously. Seth complied and even threw in some extra tobacco.

When Dardy found out about the bargain, she was livid, and she knew Galegenoh would be too. She knew she was safe with the Cherokee, and she cared for Galegenoh. Also, now she was a marked woman, tattooed as the property of an Indian man. Among whites, she would be looked upon for the rest of her life as used goods. Only among the Cherokee was such a tattoo considered a source of pride.

She appealed to the chief, but he told her she should be among her own people. Even if he did not send her away with the long hunters now, he explained, soon word would spread of her presence in the camp and white soldiers would come for her.

At sunrise the next morning, Dardy and the three long hunters left for what would be the next adventure in her life, one she did not welcome. She left with only her deerskin dress and pants, a blanket, and a deerskin coat; actually, it was a cape that had a hole cut in it for her head and hung down to cover most of her body. The weather was still very cold, especially at higher elevations, and she was grateful to have the cape and the hat Galegenoh had made her from beaver pelts. She had also been given the clothes she was captured in, although she no longer desired to wear them.

Each of the long hunters carried a rifle and had another rifle strapped onto his horse and a pistol tucked into his belt. The belt, which was always tied behind, served several purposes besides that of holding a coat together. Mittens and a bullet bag hung from the front; to the right were suspended a hatchet and a long knife, usually referred to as a scalping knife. The men kept their arms in excellent, ready shape for quick reloading when hunting an animal. Usually two men would do the firing and one would serve as a reloader.

Dardy felt safe with the woodsmen but wondered what the future would bring. It was understood that for the time being, she was the property of Seth Thomas, who had traded for her, but she suspected—correctly—that many long hunters might be inclined to share a woman the same way they portioned out food or ammunition. She was not worried. She was confident that Galegenoh would come for her.

It was warm that first night. The men were tired after a long day of riding, and all slept soundly. They planned to hunt the next day, even though they were not supposed to be hunting this close to the Cherokee, so they would not be traveling.

On the second night, Seth came over to where Dardy was sleeping, raised her blanket, and lay down beside her. She woke immediately and knew what was about to happen. She did not particularly mind. While Galegenoh still treated her with respect, he had grown tired of her, and he had been paying his attentions to a young Cherokee woman who might produce him the son Dardy had not, and a full-blooded Cherokee son at that. Many nights lately, her bed had been cold, and Dardy was never a woman to let that be the case for very long. As it turned out, Seth was gentle with her, and she actually enjoyed his company.

When Galegenoh returned from his hunting trip and learned what had happened to Dardy, he immediately prepared to bring her back. It was a matter of honor. The chief strongly objected, telling him that Dardy must be allowed to return to her people. Galegenoh asked whether she went willingly; the chief answered him honestly but repeated that it was still for the best.

Galegenoh would not be dissuaded. He insisted he would go and asked if he could take three men with him.

"If you must do this," the chief answered, "you must do it alone."

Galegenoh traveled that night, following the long hunters' trail. He stopped the first night at dusk. Sitting by the fire, he reminisced about the first night with AhWeeNee, the night of the hunting celebration dance. He remembered how, after making love, they had lain entwined on his blanket until daylight. He thought about how young she was, how tender, with soft, smooth skin. Though he had indeed been growing tired of her, now he wanted her back and was determined to have her. If necessary, he would kill to get her back, but he had also brought gold to bargain for her release.

He lay down to sleep with these thoughts of her, resolving that he would leave before dawn and overtake the long hunters.

But for Galegenoh, dawn never came. In the pitch dark, his eyes popped open at the sound of a breaking twig. One of the long hunters, Franz, had seen his fire at dusk and had doubled back to see who was following them. Galegenoh never saw the knife flying through the air, but he felt it embed itself in his right shoulder, rendering his good arm useless. He reached for his tomahawk with his left hand, but Franz was on top of him with his own form of tomahawk, the hatchet all long hunters used. With one powerful swing of the hatchet, Franz opened Galegenoh's head. Then, to make sure the Indian was dead,

Franz pulled his knife from Galegenoh's shoulder and stabbed it into his chest.

Franz knew what the rings in Galegenoh's ears stood for, and he prided himself on killing an Indian who had taken so many white lives. He scalped Galegenoh and removed one of his ears, the one that, unbeknownst to Franz, contained the rings that represented the deaths of those who had shot Galegenoh's first wife. Franz also took Galegenoh's weapons and the pouch containing the gold.

CHAPTER 48

FRANZ

The streams were full of fish, game was plentiful, and travel had become much easier for Dardy as she settled into her new life. She still longed to be with the Cherokee and Galegenoh, but after many days of travel, she had realized he was not coming for her after all. Maybe the chief was right and she would be better off with her own people, but not all of them . . .

Dardy was bathing in a nearby stream one day and was startled when she saw Franz looming above her. He was on her in a flash, and she fought.

"Seth will kill you for this," she told him.

"Shut up," Franz said viciously. "If you say anything, I will tell Seth you are lying, that it was you who made the advance to me. He will beat you. It's best you say nothing."

Then he laughed. "Besides, Seth and I have traveled together a long time. Trust me, we have shared wenches before."

Fearing he would hurt her and that Seth would believe him, she went along, but she felt nothing but disgust.

Then one night, while the men were drinking and talking, not paying any attention to her, she noticed something glittering inside Franz's pouch. The light of the fire was bouncing off the object, and she inched closer to see what it was. The men were sitting on a boulder about twenty yards away. She moved her hand closer to open the pouch and immediately saw the gold nugget. She recognized it as Galegenoh's.

She pried the pouch open and saw an object wrapped in a small piece of deerskin; she gasped when she unwrapped it and saw what remained of an ear. She recognized the earrings as those worn by her Indian lover. He had come for her after all.

Her eyes filled with tears, but her heart filled with anger and a desire for revenge.

The next morning, Seth and the other hunter, Uriah, left early to scout the trail, making sure it was safe to pass. It happened to be Franz's turn to stay and prepare the camp for travel. When it seemed likely that Seth would not return and that she would be traveling with Franz to meet him, Dardy set her plan into action. She approached Franz.

"Do I have time to go to the stream and bathe before we leave?"

"Sure, take your time, missy," he said with a small grin.

She looked him in the eye seductively as she walked toward the stream. After being in the water only a short time, she heard him approach. As he walked up, she came out of the water completely nude.

"So you enjoyed old Franz after all!" Franz said with a big smile.

He was already removing his clothes. She helped him, telling him to lie down on his back. She straddled him and leaned forward as if to kiss him. When he closed his eyes, instead of feeling her warmth as she lowered herself to his manhood, he felt the blade of his scalping knife buried deep in his throat. He frantically grabbed his throat. Blood was gushing everywhere. With her next blow, Dardy drove the blade deep into his stomach. She repeated this until movement stopped.

He was still breathing, but she did not finish him; she wanted him to die slowly. When it was obvious he was gone, she dragged his body to the stream, where the strong current carried it away. She bathed, dried off, and went back to camp.

When Seth returned and asked about Franz, she simply said he had left that morning and had not returned. She told him that Franz had said he would catch up with them later that day or the next. Franz had wandered off before and stayed away for a couple of days, so Seth was not surprised. After all, they were in safe territory now. Nothing was likely to happen this close to Glover Station.

From then on, Dardy stayed as close to Seth as she could. He thought he had won her over. He did not know of Galegenoh's or Franz's murders; he did not know that Dardy was heartbroken and homesick for the Cherokee. Seth was contented. It was now spring, and game was abundant. The streams were somewhat of an eating frenzy every spring before the fish went on their nests. Seth assumed that Franz would meet them at Glover Station.

They were making good time, and new life was springing up everywhere, including in Dardy's womb.

By April, the party had reached Kentucky. They were heading north by northwest to Fort Boonesborough. Soon they would arrive in Green County at Glover Station, named after John Glover, a long hunter who had once traveled with Seth Thomas. John Glover had settled in the area due to its proximity to the river and bottomland. He had tried to get Seth to settle there too, but Seth was not interested in farming or raising livestock.

From Glover Station, they planned to head up to Floyd's Fork and on to the Ohio River. Seth had heard of travel on the river and wanted to explore that possibility. It was said that they could travel the river more safely and easily than riding through the mountains and that the land around the river was rich in game. The river also helped protect travelers from being surprised by Indians or "highwaymen," a name given to ruffians along the Wilderness Trail.

They arrived at Glover Station in May of 1822. By this time, Dardy was no longer questioning her condition; she was definitely with child. Up until now, she had been able to conceal her size with clothing and blankets. She confronted Seth and told him she was pregnant with his child, even though she knew it was possible that the baby belonged to Franz.

The next day, he told her he was leaving her in Green County.

"I will come back for you by Christmas," he said, "but a flatboat is no place for a woman who is going to have a baby. It's easier than the trail, but it would not be pleasant for you and the baby, and there would be no one to help you when it is time for the baby to come. There is a doctor near Glover Station."

As he walked away, he added, "My friend John Glover owns a stillhouse on the outskirts of town where you can stay until I return."

Dardy ran to him, grabbed his arm, and pleaded, "Please, Seth, let me go with you. I promise I will be no problem. Please don't leave me here alone."

He looked down at her.

"Dardy, I'm sorry, but you cannot go. The trip would be too difficult for you and the baby. Believe me, it would not be pleasant. Plus, your presence would be a burden on the other men on the flatboat. Besides, there will be plenty of other women at the stillhouse, and John will make sure they help you."

He then got on his horse, which was already packed, and headed to the river. Over his shoulder, he shouted, "See you at Christmas."

Dardy boarded the wagon waiting to take her to the stillhouse, located on the outskirts of Glover Station but still in Green County. When she arrived, she was greeted by a matronly woman who looked to be of Scandinavian descent. The woman was in her forties, somewhat portly but attractive, clad in a dress with a top that revealed much of her very large breasts.

Dardy looked around at the interior of the stillhouse. As she would later learn, it had been built in 1811 as a rectangular, two-story, rough-cut stone building, with a gabled wooden shingle roof. The first floor was made up of a wooden bar with a brass footrail and a half-dozen round tables with four or five chairs around each. The floor was rough wooden boards nailed to beams set in sand. On the back wall was an old piano that no one really knew how to play. However, it was one of the first versions of the player piano, so it had the capacity to play on its own. The piano had been burned in a fire and was worse for wear, but it still played and was in good enough condition for the stillhouse and the people who frequented it, mostly rowdies from the area and travelers passing through.

The still was on the second floor, as were three bedrooms where patrons enjoyed considerably more than a good night's sleep.

"Your room is upstairs," the woman told Dardy. "You can stay there to sleep but must be willing to get out when one of the other girls needs it."

Dardy did not understand, but she needed a place to stay and would agree to just about anything.

"You will earn your keep by keeping the place clean, especially the bedrooms after the girls leave for the night. Any questions?"

"What is your name?" Dardy asked.

"I'm known around here as Ginger," the woman said. "That's all you really need to know."

"May I go to my room now?" Dardy asked. "I'm very tired."

"Yes," Ginger answered, "but get your rest now, because you will have to be out of the room by dark. Tonight will be busy."

As Dardy walked away, Ginger told her, "By the way, if you want, I can help you get rid of that swelling in your stomach."

Dardy did not answer. She remembered the words of Seth: how the river trip would not be pleasant and how he would be back for her at Christmas. Her reaction might have been different if she could have predicted the future . . .

CHAPTER 49

1822: Pleasant Sadler

Pleasant Sadler was born in the stillhouse on November 2, 1822, six months after Dardy arrived in Green County. His was a difficult birth. Dardy was young and small, and the baby's head stayed in the birth canal too long. She sat in a chair with her legs bent and spread, the midwife kneeling between her legs, telling her to push. Ginger held her from behind, and two other girls held and pulled her arms straight out.

At that time, death was common during childbirth for both the mother and the baby. Many mothers died from infections introduced by the dirty hands of midwives and doctors. About twenty-five percent of marriages were childless due to babies dying during childbirth, and many children survived birth but died young; three out of ten would die before they were five. This attrition was mainly among enslaved people, indentured servants, and lower-class whites.

There was also no anesthetic available. Dardy was screaming, and the midwife was screaming even louder, saying she must push harder or the baby would die. She also knew that even if the baby lived, it had a high possibility of being brain-damaged.

The baby's head finally made it through after several hours of pushing, but there was still more to be done, the cutting of the cord and delivery of the placenta. The midwife completed her job efficiently. Midwives were usually local women with children of their own. They learned midwifery as apprentices, as did many physicians. For their work, midwives might receive modest monetary compensation; however, they might be paid with a chicken or household goods. In this case, the midwife had her eye on some authentic Indian blankets. Dardy was glad to make the trade. She had nothing else.

So the baby was born in a stillhouse, delivered by a midwife, a madam, and two whores. Dardy named the baby Seth Pleasant Sadler after his father and his father's favorite word, "Pleasant." He would be called "Pleasant" because getting him into this world certainly hadn't been.

Dardy stayed on at the stillhouse, cleaning the rooms where the girls would take men in the evening. The girls, some younger than she, paid Pleasant a lot of attention; they were whores, but they were still girls, and they liked babies. So Pleasant got a lot of attention when he was a baby, probably too much; the girls soon spoiled him by giving him anything he wanted.

It was soon obvious that he was a self-centered child and wanted what he wanted when he wanted it. By three, he was pretty much out of control, and by five he was a regular hellion. By this time, he had figured out that his mother had very little authority over him, as he could go to Ginger or the girls and get whatever he wanted.

Actually, this didn't bother Dardy, who was also self-centered and very pleasure-minded. She was glad to have the girls raise him so she could pursue her own desires.

By this time, she was almost positive that Pleasant was not Seth's son. She had so hoped the baby would somehow belong to Galegenoh, but she had known that was probably not the case, since he had been gone on a hunting expedition when she'd left with Seth. Regardless of Pleasant's parentage, Dardy felt she needed Seth to care for and protect them both, but it had been over four years now and not a word from him. She wondered whether he was still alive.

It was apparent that Pleasant was the son of Franz. He looked more and more like him. Both Franz and Seth had had dark hair and blue eyes, but Franz's eyes were dark and menacing, a cold blue. Sometimes when Pleasant was upset and glared at her with his menacing, cold blue eyes, it would bring chills to her, as it reminded her so much of the evil Franz.

She often thought back to the look on Franz's face the day she buried the knife in his throat. She felt no remorse; he had killed the only man she had ever had real feelings for and the only who'd had feelings for her. She was heartsick when she thought about him. If she had just been gone from camp the day Seth came, she would still be back with Galegenoh and the Cherokee.

CHAPTER 50

BELL'S PROPOSITION

There had been other men in Dardy's life during her years at the stillhouse, men traveling through who had paid her attention instead of going to the whores. Mostly they were heading west, but some would be returning to Virginia or Ohio.

Dardy desperately wanted to get out of the stillhouse, and she hoped one of the men would take her with him. She wanted a place of her own for herself and Pleasant. But none of the men she met were about to take on a tattooed woman with a bastard child. They were only interested in one thing from her, and she rarely disappointed them. They would leave her money and other items of value, sometimes even food. Her encounters with these men were risky, though, because she didn't pay the house a cut of her earnings, and John Glover would have run her off if he'd found out. Ginger would have made sure of that. So Dardy got away with a couple of flings by going out for a while during the night while the girls were busy with paying customers.

When Pleasant was almost six years old, John Glover passed the stillhouse along to a local ruffian named Jason Bell. Bell had not bought the house outright, as he had very little means, just his small farm outside of town. He had bet his farm against the stillhouse in a poker game, and he had won, an event that would later prove to alter many lives, including Dardy's.

Soon, Bell had been running the house for about a year. The girls were making more money than ever before. Ginger wanted Dardy to come to work for her, but Dardy continued to try for a stable relationship, even marriage, so that she could get out of the stillhouse and take Pleasant with her. Deep down, too, she still thought Seth would show up someday, and she didn't want him finding her whoring.

Dardy knew Jason Bell fancied her, and she was determined to milk the opportunity for all it was worth. She knew when he would be coming in, always on Tuesday nights, and she would make sure she looked especially nice. She had become a very attractive woman; she would have been a nice catch for many a young man if it hadn't been for her tattoo.

The tattoo didn't bother Bell. It wasn't because he was understanding or forgiving of her past; he was a person of low character. It was because he saw her as his own "squaw," a prize to show off to his buddies.

Dardy teased and flirted with Bell, but she did not give in to his desires. She knew that Bell had sex once or twice a week with the whores, and if she gave in to him, she would be just another such experience. Shrewdly, she was holding out for a marriage proposal.

She approached him one night before he visited the girls and presented him with the arrangement that she would provide everything the girls did for him and more. She also told him sex would be more exciting with her because she would enjoy it herself, unlike the whores. He liked the idea of not paying, even though he got a discount because while he had to pay Ginger her cut, he didn't have to pay the house's cut.

"So what's the deal?" he asked.

"I want a father for my son and a home where he can grow up," Dardy said. "That's all I ask. We need to get out of this place. I will care for you, cook for you, take care of your house, even work with the animals. I can milk cows, slop hogs, and feed chickens. I can also shoot as good as any man. And I can pleasure you in ways that you have never dreamed of, things I learned from the Cherokee."

She moved closer to him as she said this, raising on her toes to kiss him.

Bell, who was already fifty-five years old, told her he would consider her proposal but needed to try out what he was buying before he bought it. She kissed him again, passionately; he reached down to raise her skirt, but she backed away and said, looking down at his obvious arousal, "You need to take that to one of the girls. For me, it will require marriage."

Smiling, she walked away, adding, "Let me know what you decide."

A little while later, there was a knock at her door; she opened it to find Bell standing there. Then she knew she was going to get what she wanted.

"I've taken a liking to that boy of yours," he said, "and it would be nice to have a woman around the farm. Never been a husband before, not sure I'll be a good one, but if you are still interested, then I'll marry you. You and the boy can get out of the stillhouse and come live on the farm, although I'm not sure the boy will want to. I think he kind of likes it here. He gets a lot of attention from the girls, you know. You also gotta know that I like my freedom to come and go as I please. I have interests outside the farm, and sometimes I will be gone for a day or two."

Dardy thought about the rumors she had heard about the rustling and robbing by Bell and some of his friends.

"I like to get out and have a drink with the boys every now and then," he continued, walking into the room and pouring himself a whiskey from the bottle on the dresser. "Sometimes the boys have whores come and drink with us. You gotta be willing to go along with that."

She smiled.

"Jason," she said, "the Indians once called me 'Spantsa.' Do you know what that means?"

"Hell, no," he answered. "I don't know Injun talk."

"It means unquenchable lust," Dardy said. "I promise you, you will have no energy left for whores."

He laughed. "That's fine by me, young lady. I'll line up the preacher."

A couple of days later, they were married by a justice of the peace. The ceremony was performed at the stillhouse. It was not unusual for people who hardly knew each other to get married. Like this marriage, many marriages were done for convenience. There were many "mail-order brides." Men who headed west for land or to mine gold often had trouble finding women. They would place ads in newspapers in the east and in other places, like church bulletins. Many women were just as desperate, especially in the years after the war, in which so many men had been killed. They would often lie about their circumstances to secure a husband; they sometimes showed up with an unexpected child or two. Of course, the women were also many times surprised to see a dirty old miner instead of the young man they'd been promised. Often, these arrangements ended before a wedding could take place; some mail-order brides ended up marrying different men than the ones who had sent for them.

So, all in all, Dardy Sadler and Jason Bell felt they had done fine, both seeming to have gotten what they wanted.

CHAPTER 51

LEAVING THE STILLHOUSE

After the short ceremony and some visiting and drinking with the "girls" and some of the locals, Bell was anxious to consummate the marriage.

"Let's go to the farm," he said to Dardy. "I will come back later for Pleasant."

She agreed, and Bell was not disappointed in his first night of marriage, though he had to wait until Dardy prepared herself. After bathing, Dardy applied a tincture she had made of gallium trifloral, also known as bedstraw, an herb used by the Indians as a perfume; it was believed to keep their men by their sides. She also burned in the bedroom the dried leaves of a plant the Indians called "fuzzy weed." It was believed to be a plant of magic and desires. The Cherokee believed that if they visualized what they wanted in their lives, the smoke of fuzzy weed would carry their desires out into the world for manifestation.

Dardy then dressed for the occasion in an outfit given to her by the Cherokee. Her dress was a white-gold color, made of deer hide, cut low in the front. Around her neck she wore a Cherokee necklace with a blue medallion. Around her waist was a band of white beads with small blue medallions hanging from them. Around her head was a band of gold beads; in the back, white feathers dangled from them.

Bell could hardly believe his eyes when Dardy finally invited him into the bedroom; he knew he had made the right decision. He told her she looked beautiful and started walking toward her. She raised her hand and stopped him.

"Wait," she said.

At first, he didn't like it. He thought he had waited long enough.

"Why?"

"Hold out your hands and put your palms up," she said.

He did as she requested, not taking his eyes off her breasts, which were bulging from her dress, the skin glistening from the sparkling fire. He felt her take one of his hands in hers and she rubbed on a perfumed oil with a very pleasant aroma. Then she did the same with his other hand and applied some to each of his ears. His eyes closed as he felt her hands open his shirt and apply the perfume to his bare chest. Then she whispered in his ear.

"The perfume is columbine," she said. "It is believed that when a man wears this perfume, his woman will succumb to his power. I now succumb to your power."

And she took back his hands and placed them on her breasts. As she did so, thoughts of Seth and of Galegenoh ran through her mind, but she knew neither would ever again be part of her life and that now she belonged to this man thirty years her senior.

After a couple of hours of lovemaking, Bell told her that he would go back and get her son. Apparently the magic she had tried so hard to kindle had already worn off, because that was the last she saw of him that night; neither he nor the boy made it back. It turned out Bell had run into some of his rowdy buddies and started drinking with them; he ended up passing out and sleeping in one of the whores' rooms.

When Bell and the boy arrived the next morning, nothing was said, but he knew she was upset.

"I told you I need my freedom," he said.

She did not respond, but proceeded to fix them breakfast, thinking to herself that this freedom thing could work both ways . . .

CHAPTER 52

THE GROOMING

Pleasant was eleven years old now, and he and Bell had become fairly close. Bell took him along to many different places, mostly adult places. Cockfights went on around Green County, and Bell liked to bet on them. He would take Pleasant with him and teach him the ropes.

A cockfight is a blood sport between two gamecocks, held in a ring called a ring pit. The gamecocks are groomed and trained for two years prior to entering the ring. They possess congenital aggression toward all males of the same species. Wagers are made on the fight, and often the cocks fight until one of them dies or is critically injured.

Pleasant loved to go to fights with Bell and became engrossed in them. He would cheer for his favorite bird to kill the other one, becoming very upset if his bird lost. Once he was so upset about his bird losing that he entered the pit and stomped to death the winning bird, who was already badly injured.

Bell also taught Pleasant to play poker; he would take him to the stillhouse and let him sit at the table and watch. Soon Pleasant was playing poker with a couple of friends in town. He was much better at it than they were, and he would often cheat to win, something else his stepfather had taught him. He was always bringing home his winnings, usually not money but pocketknives, slingshots, and articles of clothing.

The worst thing Bell did with the boy, though, was to teach him to steal outright. Soon he was stealing chickens and other animals from nearby farms.

Pleasant was becoming a product of both genetics and environment; he was stocky and strong like his father and had become as mean and cruel as both father and stepfather. By the time he was twelve, Dardy had absolutely no control over him. He and Jason came and went as they pleased, always expecting her to be there when they needed her to wait on them.

This went on for another couple of years, with Pleasant getting meaner and meaner. Rumor had it that he would find a stray dog or cat and kill it just for fun. It was said that once he set a dog on fire and watched it burn. Another time, he tied two cats' tails together with rope and hung them over a fence rail; they fought, bit, and scratched each other until they both died.

Pleasant was fourteen the day the local sheriff, William Huff, whom everyone in the county called Sheriff Willy, and two deputies rode up to the farm and told Bell that they were there to arrest Pleasant.

"What for?" Bell asked.

"For the murder of a slave about three miles south of here," Sheriff Willy answered.

"Who says so?"

"He and another boy were seen hanging around the Evans farm

the day it happened. Daniel Kessler saw them and reported it when he heard about the boy being beat to death."

"So what?" Bell answered. "No court is going to convict a white boy for protecting himself from some colored man."

"The boy was only twelve years old, Jason. That boy of yours will have to account for his death. Mr. Evans doesn't want an uprising from his slaves and other slaves in the area. You know how they are getting these days. So bring Pleasant on out here."

"What is he being charged with?" Bell asked. "I know it ain't for murder, not for just killing a colored boy. Slaves don't count as people under the law."

"No, they don't, or else I'd charge your boy with manslaughter at least," the sheriff said. "The charge is destruction of private property."

Dardy was crying as they led her son away with his hands tied behind his back. The sheriff helped him onto the horse.

"Don't worry, Mom," Pleasant said as he was taken away. "I will be back before nightfall tomorrow. They won't do anything to me. That black bastard started the fight."

But the other boy who had been with Pleasant that day, Lewis White, testified against him. Lewis told the court that he had begged Sadler to stop beating the boy, but to no avail.

"We were hanging out over by the Evans farm, on the back side, where sometimes the sheep graze," he said. "Sadler was trying to get me to go with him to steal one of those sheep. I don't reckon we would have really done it, but we were talking about it. That's when we saw the boy, who I guess was watching the sheep. He was staring at us.

"Sadler hollered at him, 'What you looking at, boy?' And the boy said, 'Nothing Master Evans can't do without. You all best move on before I go get him.' Sadler told him, 'Come over here a minute, boy,' but the boy didn't move. So Sadler jumped the fence.

"'What are you accusing us of?' he asked.

"'You got no business being in here,' the boy said.

"That's when Sadler stepped up closer to him, and the boy pushed him back some. Sadler became enraged and said 'Boy, don't you know that it's against the law for a slave to touch a white man?' The boy stood his ground, but that was a mistake. Sadler hit him in the face, knocking him down. The boy got up and ran right toward Sadler, with his head down, and tackled him, knocking him to the ground. They rolled around for a bit, but Sadler ended up on top and straddled the boy, pinning his arms down with his knees.

"And then he hit the boy with his fists, over and over, until that boy stopped moving. He was still groaning when he left; he must have died a few minutes after. And I guess Mr. Kessler saw us leaving, even though he didn't see the fight."

This was Daniel Kessler, the other witness to testify against Pleasant that day. He had indeed seen Lewis and Pleasant rushing away from the Evans farm, and Pleasant had been disheveled and spattered with blood.

So Pleasant was convicted of destroying private property. He got only a year in a labor camp, about the same as if he had killed someone's cow.

Dardy decided that she had experienced enough from these two men. Bell had never treated her right, and he had ruined Pleasant. She joined a group of Quakers heading to the Ohio River. They were headed to Pennsylvania, but Dardy was not. In fact, no one ever knew where she went. Many felt she had gone back to live out her life with the Cherokee. She was never seen or heard from by white people again.

PART FOUR

CHAPTER 53

1838: Mattie's Story

Mattie Kessler was soon to turn nineteen. While a few of her friends were already married or were planning to marry, she showed little interest in the local prospects. Being Daniel's last child, she was spoiled rotten by him. Two years earlier, on her birthday, he had given her a horse. She loved that horse dearly, and most of her spare time was spent grooming, feeding, and riding him. Much like Mattie, the horse was good-natured. She named him Good Fellow.

When Mattie wasn't caring for her horse, she was doing domestic chores; she had been well schooled in them by her mother. She and Daniel were the only ones still living in the main house. All of her siblings except Henry had moved on. Henry still assisted Daniel in running the farm, but he mainly worked his own plot of land, and he and his wife and children had their own house.

Mattie felt a strong responsibility to Daniel, especially now that he was older and widowed. She had noticed his health had waned some in the past couple of years; he just couldn't do as much as he had. She thought about how he was when she was a child: a strapping, able-bodied man who could work hard for many hours a day.

Mattie and Daniel still had strong ties to their country church, where they attended every Sunday and also on Wednesdays for an evening prayer service.

One Wednesday night, someone Mattie did not know walked into the church. As the service began, she could hardly keep her eyes off him. He was handsome and well groomed. She could tell he was a member of the White family, because he resembled his brothers and his mother Lucinda. He was taller and more mature than his brothers, but he had the same light hair with a tint of red.

At the end of the service, she was taken aback by the fact that he was walking toward her with Lucinda, whom she knew fairly well and had always liked.

"Mattie, how are you?" Lucinda greeted her. "I want you to meet my eldest son, William. I know you have met my other two sons, Lewis and John; they are usually with me at evening service. Tonight I finally persuaded William to join me."

Mattie fumbled her words but was finally able to get out, "Nice to meet you, William, and I hope to see you at Sunday service."

William was not much of a churchgoer, but he was certainly happy that he had attended that night. He was already smitten, enamored with Mattie's good looks. He wanted to get to know more about her. To Mattie, he seemed a little mysterious. She hoped she would see him again. And she did. He continued to attend church, and eventually he started to stop by the farm. They would sit and talk on the front porch. Before long, they were meeting whenever and wherever they could.

Daniel was none too happy about the courtship. He didn't like

William. He thought that if it weren't for Mattie, he would refer to the boy as "the scoundrel." Daniel had heard about William's carrying on down at a rough local place called the stillhouse, associating with loose women, drinking too much shine, fighting, and getting into trouble. And William had few skills or means to support a wife. Daniel wanted Mattie to marry someone who would be interested in farming and who would stay on the farm that Mattie would inherit with her brother Henry.

Unfortunately, Daniel's worst fears became reality when one Sunday after service, William asked to speak with him alone. He asked Daniel for Mattie's hand in marriage.

"You have only known each other for a few months," Daniel argued. "Why not give it time? And how will you support her? Your reputation in the county is not good. Word is that you are even in trouble with the law for some of your rowdy behavior."

"That was all in the past," William said. "I have changed, and I love Mattie. Just this week, I secured a job at the feed store. Mr. Kessler, your blessing would mean so much to us, especially to Mattie."

He could sense that Daniel was starting to come around.

"We can live with my mother in town until we have the means to acquire a house of our own," he added. "My mother dearly loves Mattie, as do both of my brothers. She will be well taken care of, I promise."

Daniel reluctantly assented, and the wedding took place on a bright and beautiful Saturday on the lawn of Daniel's house. Many friends and neighbors came, along with Mattie's siblings and their families. The preacher Joshua Berthold was there, as was Sheriff Willy. They all brought food; it filled three large tables. There was corn liquor and shine and plenty of the beer Lucinda bottled at her place, where she ran a small "tippling house." Henry had slaughtered a hog that winter and still had a big country ham, which he brought. Some of the neighbors brought fried chicken. The Kesslers boiled a big kettle of corn on the cob and served baked beans with fatback bacon. There were boiled turnips with carrots and onions. And it was all topped off with several cakes and pies.

Daniel could see that Mattie was happy and very much in love.

Mattie was content, and she adjusted to married life quite easily, so much so that Daniel admitted to her that maybe he had misjudged William. All Daniel cared about was making sure she was treated well. He was glad that Lucinda doted on Mattie, calling her "the daughter that I never had but always wanted."

Lucinda was still a young and healthy woman, in her early forties. She had married a somewhat older man, and upon his death he had left her with a modest amount of wealth, enough for a widow and three sons to live comfortably. So there was no problem welcoming a new member of the family.

Indeed, Lucinda hoped that her eldest son and her new daughter-in-law would soon give her grandbabies. She would often tell the couple to go and spend some time alone together.

"I can manage the tippling house," she would say cheerfully. "After all, I managed for years on my own."

Encouraged, they would pack a picnic basket and a blanket and head out to find a remote, beautiful spot. Before long, passion would overtake them, their bodies responding, never tiring, always desiring more from each other.

CHAPTER 54

ALABAMA

What neither Daniel nor Lucinda knew was that William and Mattie had already made love several times before they were married. At their wedding, Mattie had been three months pregnant. To Mattie, the pregnancy had been a welcome surprise; motherhood was something she had always wanted. But she had been reluctant to tell William, not wanting him to feel forced into marrying her. After she had told him, though, he had seemed to welcome the news.

Young Will was born almost six months after the wedding. Daniel was furious when he first realized Mattie had been pregnant before her marriage, but he decided to let it go and not say anything. His anger would only cause Mattie pain, and she seemed so happy and content with her life as a wife and mother. And his anger didn't last long after the baby was born, stealing his heart. Daniel was also reassured because William was working; all seemed to be going well.

However, Daniel was unaware that William was constantly talking about leaving and going back to Alabama, where he had lived for several years. He had connections there and felt sure he could get an overseer job on one of the cotton plantations. With increasing demand for cotton, more and more Africans were being brought to America as slaves and sold in the South. African slaves were now the preferred source of labor, since more laws were being enacted to protect indentured servants. To William, the growing plantations were a great opportunity, one that would only get bigger.

But when he told Mattie of his plans, she couldn't accept that her husband might be involved in slavery. She couldn't understand how one person could treat another with such cruelty. One night, as he again brought up the thought of leaving for Alabama, she voiced her opinion.

"Husband, I am a God-fearing woman. I love you, and I want to be with you, but I could never let young Will be a part of such a thing. I have told you the story of my grandfather. He came to America with his family as an indentured servant when he was only ten years old. It was the only way they could pay for the passage to America. I never met him, but Daddy told his story to me many times. He endured unimaginable hardships. And things are so much worse for slaves. It is difficult for me to even think of being a part of that life, knowing what my grandfather and his family went through."

William saw tears streaming down her face.

"I'm sorry," he said. "I didn't know about your grandfather. I just want to better our situation. My plans do not include living with my mother and younger brothers forever. Maybe something better will come my way. Let's see what happens."

Then he started kissing her tears away, and they made love.

While the conversation about moving to Alabama stopped for a few weeks, the issue was far from being resolved. Before long, William was again talking about leaving. And he was doing other things to upset Mattie: not coming home until late at night, if at all, and associating again with undesirable characters at the stillhouse.

Then one day William came home and told the family he would be leaving for Alabama in the morning. He said that he would send for them as soon as he was settled and had employment.

The next morning, as William loaded up his horse and prepared to leave, Mattie approached him with tears in her eyes.

"How long will it be before you send for us?"

"Before you know it, we will all be together again," William said. "Have faith in me, girl. I know what I need to do."

After saying all of his goodbyes to his mother and brothers, he hugged and kissed Mattie and young Will. Then, just like that, he rode away.

At first Mattie tried to be loyal and hopeful, but as weeks turned into months, she became worried that something terrible had happened to her husband. He did not write home, and she had no way of knowing whether he was safe or had met with some tragedy. There were so many hazards in traveling alone. Lucinda continuously tried her best to console Mattie, assuring her that William loved her and young Will and would never abandon them.

Mattie was not sure.

As time went on, she found herself spending more and more time with Daniel on the farm. Daniel loved little Will, and the boy adored his grandfather, whom he called Papa. Will had so bonded with Daniel that even though Mattie's heart ached for her husband, she was happy that Will at least had his grandfather to protect him. Soon Mattie was dividing her time evenly between Lucinda's house and Daniel's.

Then one night Mattie learned that the White family was planning on moving to Alabama to join William. Lucinda's late husband had had family there and had encouraged her to join them. As the Whites talked, it became apparent to Mattie that her place was with her husband. She told Lucinda she would go with them. It was her only hope for reuniting with William. Lucinda and the boys assured her they would find him and they would all be together as a family once more.

Mattie continued life as usual, never letting on to Daniel that she planned to leave Green County and take young Will with her. Unfortunately, in a small community, few secrets are kept. Finally, the day came when Daniel confronted her.

"Mattie, I have heard that you are leaving with Lucinda and her boys, going to Alabama. Why haven't you told me of your plans?"

In a surprised and somewhat frightened tone, Mattie replied, "I knew you would be hurt, and I just couldn't find the right time to tell you, Daddy. Please don't be mad at me."

"I'm not mad," Daniel reassured her, "but I am wondering: you've not heard from that husband of yours. How can you be sure you will find him?"

"Lucinda and the boys have assured me that we will find him and all will be back the way it was," she replied.

Daniel looked at her with his dark blue eyes, which looked saddened by the whole affair.

"Mattie, what kind of man would leave his wife and infant son and stay away all this time without any word?" he said.

Mattie had no answer for that.

"You're a grown woman, old enough to do what you want," he said. "I can't stop you. But I will tell you that the men Lucinda has hired to get you all to Alabama, led by Carrington Simpson, are lowly rowdies who are suspected of rustling livestock in this county and others. You can't trust them."

Mattie knew Carrington Simpson. He was one of the men William had gotten into trouble with.

Seeing that her father was anxious for her safety and Will's, and knowing his heart was breaking, Mattie assured him she would not leave. Secretly, though, she was torn. Mattie had never been but a few miles away from home. Farm, church, and family were all she had ever known. But she so wanted to be with William again, to have a father for her son.

Eventually, Mattie decided to go with the Whites. But . . . something just didn't feel right to her.

CHAPTER 55

THE PLOT

Daniel was right about the three men Lucinda had hired to transport the White family to Alabama: Carrington Simpson, Pleasant Sadler, and Jason Bell. They were rowdies and rustlers. But Daniel did not know the true darkness of their natures or how far they would go for a little money.

Sadler was fifteen now, a hardened young man with many experiences and many character flaws. He was close to being sociopathic, extremely narcissistic and self-centered, carrying little about anyone or anything except his own desires, though it bothered him some that his mother was gone with no explanation. For a change, Bell had told the truth—Dardy had left of her own accord—but Sadler still thought Bell had had something to do with it. Maybe he'd killed her. Maybe he'd run her off or sold her to somebody. Sadler didn't trust Bell, but then, he really didn't trust anybody.

Still, they had stayed on Bell's farm together, though it had become run down as most of their time was spent at the stillhouse plotting illegal activities. The two men had started "striking" for Simpson, who was a local butcher and landowner. Simpson, who was shrewder than either Bell or Sadler, soon had them doing his bidding entirely. Under his plans and direction, they committed crimes such as slaughtering their neighbors' cattle and hogs, curing the meat at home, and selling Simpson the larger portion, some of which he would sell to the unwitting neighbors from whom it had been stolen.

This went on for months, with the crimes becoming more and more brazen. On a few occasions, they robbed travelers on the road, taking their valuables and money. Most of the valuables, like watches, bracelets, and necklaces, would be sold at bargain prices to men stopping at the stillhouse on their way through the county. The men would take the goods and be gone, leaving Simpson and his two strikers with the money.

One hot July night in 1838, Simpson, Sadler, and Bell were drinking at the stillhouse when Simpson mentioned that the widow Lucinda White was looking for someone to move her and her family to Alabama.

"Didn't Old Man Kessler's daughter marry William White, who used to hang around here at the stillhouse?" asked Sadler. Daniel Kessler and Lewis White, Lucinda's son, had witnessed his killing of the young black boy and had turned him in to the law and testified against him in court. This might be his opportunity for revenge.

"That's right," Simpson said. "She married William, who left for Alabama some months ago; now the family wants to join him."

Sadler remarked, "Lucinda White has a purse as long as your arm . . ."

CHAPTER 56

SUSPICION

When Daniel arrived at church on Sunday and found no Mattie, Will, Lucinda, or her two boys, he started feeling sick to his stomach. Soon, speaking with others, he was told that all had left together to travel to Alabama. He felt betrayed. How could his daughter have lied to him? It was not like her.

He returned home a lonely old man, unsure of whether he would ever see Mattie or Will again. He'd had so many plans for that boy. He had meant to teach him everything he knew about the outdoors, farming and fishing and hunting. Now he probably would not get the chance.

At least, he thought, surely when she was settled Mattie would send a letter. However, as days turned into weeks and weeks into months with no letters received, his optimism waned. It was so unlike Mattie. She was a thoughtful and caring girl. He just could not accept that she would not send word back to him of her safe arrival.

Daniel always asked anyone traveling through the county whether they had seen the White family, but none had. He sent off letters, hoping to contact William, but no response ever came. He started thinking of leaving to search for them, but then the entire burden of the farm would come to rest on Henry and his family. It would be unfair to place such a burden on them during this busy time, when all hands were needed. Also, Daniel was not in the best of health, and he was unsure whether he could make the trip.

Though he fretted every day, he decided it was best to wait. He worked hard and tried to enjoy the time he had with Henry's family, and in his spare time, he read the Bible and prayed for Mattie and Will's return.

Months passed, and still there was no word of them. Then, one Sunday after service, a woman named Regina Johnson and her daughter approached him.

"Mr. Kessler," said Regina, "as you know, I am a seamstress and have made clothes for many people in the area, especially when they want something special. Before they left town, both Lucinda White and your daughter wanted dresses made of a special fabric they had ordered through Mr. Kerry's general store.

"Mr. Kessler, what I am about to tell you upsets me something terrible. Last week I saw someone wearing the dress I made for Lucinda White. No mistaking it. It was the exact dress. I got close enough to make sure. The same fabric and a neckline with ruffled edges, just as Mrs. White had requested. I'm telling you this because the dress fabric was fairly costly and I could not understand Mrs. White giving the dress away, especially since I had just finished it right before she left on her trip. I've been trying to make sense of it all, but I can't, so I thought it best to tell you."

"Mrs. Johnson," Daniel said, "I truly appreciate you coming forward with this information, and I will give some serious thought to what you have just told me. If you should see or hear of anything else that doesn't seem right, please let me know."

Soon after this conversation, other neighbors started talking about seeing various articles of clothing which they recognized as those of the White family, such as ladies' dresses and children's clothing, being worn by the Simpson family. When questioned, Simpson simply stated that he had received the articles as partial payment for the trip to Alabama. But everyone knew Lucinda White had enough money to pay the people she'd hired; she wouldn't have needed to give them clothing.

Many started to believe that foul play had come to the White family.

One day Cyrus, a longtime friend of the Kessler family, came to the farm and told Daniel that he had seen Pleasant Sadler wearing boots that he knew belonged to Lucinda White's youngest son, Lewis.

"They were sort of fancy, Daniel, unlike what most folks wear around here," Cyrus said. "I remember the first time I saw Lewis wearing them. The boy was very proud of them and told me his mother had specially ordered them through a catalog."

But it was what Cyrus said next that prompted Daniel to take action.

"What man do you know who would be willing to give up a good pair of boots?"

The next morning, Daniel headed into town to have a visit with Sheriff Willy. Willy was already seventy-five years old and didn't have much of a job to do enforcing the law, as Green County had little crime other than what happened at the stillhouse, and he didn't bother with that, since they had their own kind of law. Still, Daniel didn't know where else to go with his concerns.

"Good morning, Daniel," said the sheriff. "What brings you to town?"

Daniel told him the story of the clothes, especially the distinctive boots that had belonged to Lewis White.

"Now, Daniel, I've heard some stories about them clothes, but Carrington says they were payment for the move," Willy replied. "You know it's not that unusual to be paid in goods for such a deed as moving someone."

"That may not be unusual, but what is unusual is for my daughter Mattie not to be in touch with me for all this time. I say something is wrong, and Carrington Simpson ought to be arrested," Daniel said sternly.

"Now, Daniel," Willy said again, "just settle down. We can't go arresting somebody just because they are wearing some clothes that they say was payment for services. Far as I know, Carrington hasn't broken any laws, even though it's suspected that he has done some rustling. As to your Mattie, we have people leave our county all the time heading west, and many times the family never hears of them again.

"You come back and see me when you have some evidence," Willy went on. "I think all you have now is some busybodies with nose trouble, trying to stir things up because they don't like Carrington Simpson and would like to see him out of the county. Can't say I blame them, but I can't arrest him without evidence.

"Now you go on back home and take care of your farm and the rest of your family, and leave the sheriffing to me."

That day Daniel returned to the farm, knowing something terrible had happened and with a resolve that he would make things right. His broken heart was slowly being replaced by anger and a desire for revenge of the wrongs he felt sure had been done to Mattie, Will, and the rest of the White family. He vowed that he would not rest until he found the truth about his daughter and grandson and took vengeance on those who might have hurt them.

CHAPTER 57

WILLIAM WHITE RETURNS

Then, to everyone's surprise, William White came back from Alabama, looking for his family. He said they had never arrived in Alabama.

"I just figured they decided not to come," he told Daniel. "I figured Mattie didn't want to have anything to do with me, since I'd stayed gone so long. I just wasn't cut out to be a husband and father."

Daniel looked at him with scorn and anger.

"You got my Mattie pregnant and then deserted her and the boy," he said. "No one heard from you for almost two years. What kind of man would do that?"

Daniel, who stood a good six inches taller than William, moved in close to him, wanting to strangle him, but in the end he couldn't do it. He just stared him down until William looked away.

"Where have you been, White?" Daniel asked. "Why have you come back now, after all this time? What have you been doing? *And where is my daughter?*"

Daniel was shouting by now. He grabbed William's shoulders and shook him. William pulled away and made sure Daniel saw the pistol in his waistband. The two men just stared at each other, neither saying anything, until William broke the silence.

"Look, Daniel," he said. "I told Mattie right from the beginning that I would marry her to give the boy a legitimate father but that I wasn't staying in Green County. I had other plans. I intended to come back and get her, but soon after I got to Alabama, I got a job as an overseer, and . . . well, I struck up a relation with the landowner's daughter. I came back here to get my mother and brothers and to get a divorce from Mattie, and then I planned to head back to Alabama. That's still what I intend to do.

"But now I have a question for you. I haven't heard from anyone for over a year. Not Mattie, not my mother or brothers. Mother, at least, would have written. I come back here and I am told that they all left for Alabama over a year ago. Then I'm told that my mother's dress has been seen worn by one of those Simpson women and my brother Lewis's boots are being worn by Pleasant Sadler, whom Lewis knew as a boy. So you tell me: Where are they? It all sounds suspicious to me. I think you need to be talking to Simpson and Sadler and to Jason Bell, Sadler's stepfather."

Daniel was listening and was starting to think more clearly now. William was right. Simpson needed to be talked to, regardless of what Sheriff Willy said.

"Will you go with me and talk to Simpson?" he asked.

"Let's do it," replied William.

CHAPTER 58

The Trunk

The two of them rode up to Simpson's farm. He came out onto his front porch, a thin man with sharp features and dark, thinning hair that he combed straight back. He was holding a shotgun. He told them to get off his land, saying that he had nothing to say to them.

This made them even more suspicious and determined, so they returned, this time with a reluctant Sheriff Willy. Again Simpson met them on the porch, but this time without the shotgun.

"Good day to you, Carrington," said Sheriff Willy. "Mind if we ask you a couple of questions?"

"I got nothing to say I haven't already said," Simpson answered.

"Tell me about that trip to Alabama when you moved Lucinda White and her boys along with Mattie and her son," Willy asked. "How much did you charge them, and how did you get paid for the trip?"

"We charged ten dollars apiece," Simpson said. "They gave us five apiece before we left and was to pay us the other five when we arrived in Alabama."

"How long did it take to make the trip?" the sheriff asked.

Simpson paused; he was looking uncomfortable, fidgeting.

"Well, my recollection is that it took us six or seven days each way," he finally replied.

"You are a damn liar, Simpson," Daniel said. "It's two hundred and sixty miles to Madison County, Alabama. My son Henry says that it would take ten to twelve days each way, and that's only if you didn't run into any difficulty."

"Tell me again about the clothing," Willy cut in. "How come we are seeing more and more of it that belonged to Lucinda White's family?"

"They bargained with us on the way, wanted to pay in goods instead of money. Simple as that," Simpson replied.

"Regina Johnson said she saw a brand-new dress she had made for Lucinda," said the sheriff. "She didn't think Lucinda would have parted with that dress."

"And Lewis would never have parted with those boots that Sadler is walking around town in!" shouted William White.

"I said my piece. Now you all get off my property," Simpson told them.

But William and Sheriff Willy kept talking to Simpson. Daniel, on the other hand, slipped away and walked out back of the house. He had an eerie feeling that there was something evil about this place, and he wanted to look around. There was a small corral and a barn in the back. Daniel walked into the barn and spotted what looked like a clothing trunk. He walked over to it and raised the lid. On the inside were carved the initials L. W.

But it was the contents of the trunk that made Daniel shiver and made blood rush to his head. His temples were pounding and his heart racing as he looked down and saw the saddle he had given Mattie for her horse Good Fellow. Daniel knew she would never have parted with that horse or saddle for any amount of money.

He also now knew that Mattie had probably never even left Green County.

CHAPTER 59

THE SEARCH

Soon after, in March of 1840, eighteen months after the Whites had disappeared, Daniel and several neighbors petitioned Justice J. D. Motley and prosecutor Isaac Gibbons to issue a warrant for the arrest of Carrington Simpson. After hearing the evidence and duly deliberating thereon, Motley and Gibbons committed Simpson to jail, to be held for trial at the next circuit court session for the murder of five persons: Lucinda White, her two younger sons, Mattie, and young Will.

Four or five days after Simpson's arrest, more than one hundred people gathered at the Green County courthouse square with the intention of combing the county for the bodies of the White family. They divided into groups. One of the men had with him a grubbing-hoe, and his group headed for the old field where the waste house stood. They had no idea of what they would find, if anything.

After what seemed like hours of going over every inch of the field, looking for any clues or signs of graves, they came upon the old waste house and the large hole in the ground. They still saw nothing. It was a hot, muggy Kentucky summer day, and there's nothing like being in ninety-degree-plus heat, plus humidity, tramping around lowlands, to test one's temper.

"This is a waste of time," said one of the men.

"There is nothing to find back here," another agreed. "They probably dumped the bodies in the river; they are long gone by now."

But Sheriff Willy, part of the search team, was not convinced. He summoned the others. "Bring that grubbing-hoe over here and let's go in the hole and dig around a bit. We are here, so we might as well try."

The man with the grubbing-hoe walked to the hole, which was covered with tobacco stalks. He made two quick licks with the hoe. The first lick . . . nothing. But the second lick . . . *clank.*

Suddenly the men were alert, staring intently at the hoe, its blade invisible under the stalks. The sheriff grabbed the handle of the hoe and lifted it out of the stalks, bringing with it something that looked like a rib from a human body. The men immediately started clearing the rubbish away. What they saw was a sickening sight. A few of the men actually did get sick, retching, at the sight of several human forms.

Alertly, Sheriff Willy instructed everyone, "Don't touch anything 'til the coroner gets here." He then sent one of the men on horseback to fetch the coroner.

Word soon got out, and the sheriff was worried that there was going to be a lynching. Sure enough, that night several men gathered at the jail, hollering at Simpson, "You're guilty, Simpson!" "You're goin' to hang!" They stayed outside the jail for over an hour but never tried to crash the door.

Within days, it was confirmed that the bodies under the tobacco stalks were indeed those of the unfortunate White family, Mattie and young Will included. Simpson still denied his part in the murders, but his many conflicting stories only strengthened the case against him. He now admitted plotting with Lucinda and Mattie to leave at night, so as to avoid Mattie's father. The plan, he said, had been to be long gone by the time Daniel got suspicious and started to look for Mattie. He still denied, however, that he'd had any part in the murders.

The sheriff knew he had the right man but worried that he could not prove it. But he and the county prosecutor agreed Simpson probably hadn't committed the murders alone. Some of the townspeople agreed, saying that the other men who'd been hired to move the family must have been involved or at least must know what had happened.

A few nights later, some regulars from the stillhouse were outside the jail.

"Where are your buddies Bell and Sadler?" one shouted. "We know you're guilty, and we know you didn't act alone!"

"No man could have done this by himself!" another shouted.

Simpson, in his cell, showed no emotion, but he was thinking. The next morning, he asked to see the sheriff.

"I've been thinking, Sheriff," he said. "Why should I be held responsible for what somebody else done?"

"You got something to say, Simpson, you'd best be saying it," Sheriff Willy replied.

"Well, you see, Sheriff, I did know some harm had come to those poor folks, but it wasn't me that perpetrated it."

"Who was it, then, you lyin' polecat?" Willy asked.

"It was Jason Bell and Pleasant Sadler who did the murdering in every instance. They now reside out in Bush Creek, about fifteen miles from here. I heard they had a cabin right on the creek; I suspect most folks out that way would know where."

Willy turned and walked out without saying another word. He obtained warrants for Bell's and Sadler's arrests and brought them in without incident. They were charged with murder and locked up. Like Simpson, they would be held over until their trial with no chance of bail.

A day or so later, Sheriff Willy made a call on Daniel at his farm. They sat on the front porch to talk.

"I'm truly sorry about Mattie and young Will," he said to Daniel, slowly, his voice cracking and his eyes glistening with tears. "Mattie was a fine young lady; we all thought highly of her. I also want to make an apology to you for not taking your concerns seriously. I was wrong, and my heart aches for your loss and for my not acting on the evidence you brought me.

"I'm an old man, Daniel, too old to be a sheriff, and the doc tells me my heart is not so good. I don't know how much time I have on this Earth, but I promise you one thing: I will not die or rest 'til I see those murdering bastards put in the ground . . . after hanging at the end of a rope."

With that, Willy stood up and headed for his horse.

Daniel did not reply to what Willy had said. He only called after him, "Be careful on the way back, Willy. Storm's supposed to be coming."

CHAPTER 60

SIMPSON'S STORY

Three days before the trial, a reporter named Jacob Todd, who wrote for the local newspaper, walked into the sheriff's office and asked if he could interview Simpson.

"Why would you want to do that, young man? He is a murdering, no-good snake in the grass," said Eric Reed, the deputy on duty, who was charged with personally seeing that nothing happened to Simpson before the trial started.

"I think the townspeople and those in surrounding counties would like to know about him," said Jacob Todd. "He is not from around these parts. I myself would like to know about him and what would possess a man to do such a thing."

Reed considered, then said, "He ain't much for talking, but I guess it would be okay if he wants to."

The deputy led the reporter back to the cell.

"This here reporter wants to talk to you, Simpson," Reed said.

"I got nothing to say to no reporter," Simpson retorted.

But the deputy walked away, saying, "You've got ten minutes."

Todd reached into his pocket, pulled out a small pouch of tobacco, and offered it to Simpson to break the ice.

"Don't mind if I do," said Simpson, accepting it.

"I would like to put your life story in my paper, the *Lexington Intelligencer*," Todd said. "It will also run in the *Louisville Weekly Journal*, the *Kentucky Register* in Elizabethtown, and the *Kentucky Yeoman* in Frankfort. And, of course, it will run in your own *Gazette* here in Green County."

Simpson was already reconsidering. He liked the idea of getting into the newspaper. He also thought that if he told his story carefully, it might help him get out of this mess.

"Can you write?" Todd asked.

"Yeah, I can write."

"Okay. I'm going to leave this pencil and paper with you. You can keep the tobacco; here are some matches. When I come back this afternoon, you have it written out and I will have it published just like you wrote it."

Simpson wrote:

I WAS BORN IN THE COUNTY OF CHESTERFIELD, VIRGINIA, ON AUGUST 10, 1782, IN THE COAL COUNTRY OF MANCHESTER, WHERE I LIVED UNTIL 1818. I THEN MOVED TO ROCKINGHAM, NORTH CAROLINA. I LIVED THERE FOR TEN YEARS AND THEN MOVED TO GREEN COUNTY, KENTUCKY, ABOUT SEVEN MILES FROM GREENSBURG. I WAS ONE OF EIGHT CHILDREN: FOUR SISTERS, BETSY, RHODY, POLLY, AND LEAR, AND THREE BROTHERS, LANGHORN, ROBERT, AND JACK. MY MOTHER'S NAME

WAS JENNY SIMPSON. SHE WAS NEVER MARRIED. MY FATHER WAS RUMORED TO BE JUDGE CARRINGTON OF VIRGINIA, FROM WHOM I TOOK MY GIVEN NAME. IN 1809, I MARRIED DICEY POWELL, DAUGHTER OF JAMES POWELL OF CHESTERFIELD.

I WAS DRAFTED INTO THE ARMY IN 1814 AT AGE THIRTY-TWO. I SOLDIERED AND MARCHED UNDER THE COMMAND OF CAPTAIN BERFOOT FOR SIX MONTHS AT CAMP HOLLY, NEAR RICHMOND. I WAS DISCHARGED DURING THE SERVICE AT CAMP HOLLY.

WHILE IN THE SERVICE I WAS NOT IDLE IN SUPPLYING MYSELF WITH ANYTHING AND EVERYTHING NEEDED WHICH FELL IN MY WAY. THE HEN-ROOSTS OF THE NEIGHBORHOOD, THE STORES OF THE COMMISSARY AND OF MY BROTHER SOLDIERS SUFFERED NO LITTLE FROM ME.

FROM THE TIME I WAS TEN YEARS OF AGE TO THE TIME I WENT INTO THE ARMY, I WAS ENGAGED IN THE GROCERY BUSINESS, FIRST AS AN ASSISTANT TO MY BROTHER JACK AND AFTERWARD AS PARTNER, THEN SOLE PROPRIETOR. AFTER THIS, I CONNECTED BUTCHERING TO MY BUSINESS, IN WHICH I CONTINUED UNTIL I LEFT CHESTERFIELD. THE STORE I OCCUPIED FOR BUSINESS WAS RENTED, AND I OCCUPIED THE SPACE FOR FIFTEEN YEARS AT FIFTY DOLLARS PER YEAR. I WAS NOT SLOW IN FORMING ACQUAINTANCES OF DIFFERENT TYPES OF PEOPLE, ANYONE WHO WOULD LEND THEMSELVES TO BE

MY INSTRUMENTS OF STEALING. I FORMED AN ALLIANCE WITH AN OVERSEER NAMED ARCHIBALD CASEY WHO WORKED FOR COLONEL THOMAS HARRIS. ARCHIBALD SUPPLIED ME WITH AN ABUNDANCE OF CORN, OATS, AND WHEAT STOLEN FROM HARRIS AND OTHERS. I WAS SUPPLIED THIS WAY FOR SEVERAL YEARS WITH ALMOST EVERYTHING I NEEDED.

COLONEL HARRIS HAD A WEALTHY SISTER BY THE NAME OF NANCY, WHO OWNED A NEGRO MAN NAMED PETER, WHO WAS AN EFFICIENT STRIKER FOR ME AND SUPPLIED ME WITH SHEEP, HOGS, CATTLE, TURKEYS, ETC. I FORMED A PARTNERSHIP WITH A MAN NAMED CHELSEY WOOLDRIDGE, WHO LIVED NEAR THE LINE OF POWHATAN COUNTY AND WHO WAS EVERY BIT AS BAD A MAN AS MYSELF. TO CARRY ON THE BUSINESS, WE EACH PUT UP FORTY DOLLARS.

WE WERE DOING PRETTY WELL BUT WANTED TO MAKE MONEY FASTER, SO WE TALKED PETER INTO LEAVING HIS MISTRESS AND COMING INTO OUR SERVICE. HE CONSENTED, AND WE KEPT HIM CONCEALED FOR ABOUT EIGHTEEN MONTHS. DURING THAT TIME, HE BROUGHT SHEEP, CATTLE, GOATS, ETC., STOLEN FROM HIS MISTRESS AND OTHER FARMS IN THE AREA. AFTER GETTING WHAT SERVICE WE COULD OUT OF HIM, WE DECIDED TO TURN HIM INTO MONEY. IT WAS AGREED THAT WOOLDRIDGE SHOULD TAKE HIM OFF TO KENTUCKY AND SELL HIM AND THEN RETURN AND DIVIDE THE MONEY WITH ME, BUT THAT WAS THE LAST I EVER HEARD OF WOOLDRIDGE OR PETER.

THE LAST DIFFICULTY THAT OCCURRED WITH ME IN VIRGINIA WAS CONCERNING SOME SHEEP. A MAN BY THE NAME OF KIDD AND A FREE NEGRO BY THE NAME OF DAVID LANDRUM PROCURED FOR ME SOME STOLEN SHEEP, AROUND TWELVE TO FIFTEEN OF THEM. I TOOK THEM TO RICHMOND AND SOLD THEM FOR A GOOD PRICE. BEFORE THEY DELIVERED THEM TO ME, ONE OF THE SHEEP GOT AWAY AND ENDED UP MIXING WITH SHEEP ON THE FARM OF ERASMUS REAMS. DAVID WENT BACK TO GET HIM AND WAS CAUGHT AND TOLD THEM I HAD SOLD THE OTHER SHEEP IN RICHMOND. I WAS LATER FOUND GUILTY BY A GRAND JURY, AND AN ARREST WARRANT WAS ISSUED. TO AVOID THIS, I FLED TO NORTH CAROLINA.

I BOUGHT LAND IN NORTH CAROLINA FROM A MAN NAMED PIRTLE AND LIVED ON IT UNTIL I MOVED TO KENTUCKY, BUT I NEVER PAID FOR IT, AND PIRTLE TOOK IT BACK. WHILE LIVING THERE, I RETURNED TO VIRGINIA SEVERAL TIMES BUT SOON WAS ARRESTED. KIDD AND LANDRUM FROM TIME TO TIME WERE SUPPLYING ME WITH STOLEN GOODS. ERASMUS REAMS, WHOSE NAME I MENTIONED BEFORE, WAS THE OVERSEER OF JUDGE FLEMING OF VIRGINIA.

PREVIOUS TO THIS LAST INCIDENT MENTIONED, I HAD SEVERAL TIMES BEEN ARRESTED AND TRIED BEFORE AN ENQUIRING COURT FOR PETTY OFFENSES, SOME OF WHICH I WAS GUILTY OF, BUT I ALWAYS MANAGED TO ESCAPE PUNISHMENT. MY DEEDS WERE GENERALLY DONE IN THE NEIGHBORHOOD IN

WHICH I LIVED. ON ONE OCCASION, UPON A CHARGE OF ROBBERY, ALTHOUGH INNOCENT, I WOULD HAVE BEEN FOUND GUILTY HAD IT NOT BEEN FOR AN ALIBI PROVIDED BY A MINISTER OF HIGH CHARACTER, BENJAMIN WATKINS, WHO STATED THAT ON THE NIGHT OF THE ALLEGED ROBBERY, I WAS AT A MEETING AT ANDERSON JOHNSON'S, WHERE HE PREACHED AND I SAT UNDER THE PULPIT ALL THE TIME. PREACHER WATKINS'S TESTIMONY SAVED MY HIDE THAT TIME. I'VE ALWAYS BEEN ABLE TO GET OUT OF SCRAPES WITH THE LAW.

WHILE IN NORTH CAROLINA, I PERPETRATED A GOOD MANY PETTY OFFENSES WITHOUT DETECTION, ALTHOUGH ONCE I WAS ARRESTED FOR HORSE STEALING. I WENT ON ONE OCCASION TO A BARBECUE WITH WILLIAM WORTLEY. WE REMAINED ON THE GROUNDS UNTIL AFTER DARK, WHEN WE EACH STOLE A HORSE. THE HORSE TAKEN BY ME BELONGED TO A MAN NAMED WILLIAM BETHEL. ON OUR WAY, WE OVERTOOK THE OWNER OF THE HORSE I HAD STOLEN. HE IMMEDIATELY RECOGNIZED NOT ONLY THE HORSE BUT MYSELF AS WELL. BETHEL CAUGHT HOLD OF THE BRIDLE OF THE HORSE AND STOPPED HIM, AND I DISMOUNTED AND MADE OFF AT ONCE. BETHEL AFTERWARD OBTAINED A WARRANT AND HAD ME ARRESTED, BUT NO ONE APPEARING AT THE TRIAL TO PROSECUTE, I WAS DISCHARGED.

I CONTINUED TO GET IN TROUBLE AFTER I MOVED TO KENTUCKY. I WAS ARRESTED FOR STEALING HOGS AND SENTENCED TO PRISON BUT WAS RELEASED AFTER A SHORT

TIME. I HAD A MISCHIEVOUS DISPOSITION. ONE NIGHT WHILE DRINKING AT THE STILLHOUSE WITH BELL AND SADLER, THEY TALKED A YOUNG MAN INTO LETTING THEM INITIATE HIM INTO THE MASONS. SADLER AND I STRIPPED HIM, SOAKED HIM WITH SOAP, DUNKED HIM IN A DEEP TROUGH OF WATER, AND THEN BRANDED HIM WITH A HOT IRON. BELL WAS PRESENT BUT DID NOT PARTICIPATE. THE YOUNG MAN WANTED NO MORE TO DO WITH THE MASONS.

SOMETIMES SADLER AND BELL WOULD JOIN UP WITH ME TO STEAL A NEIGHBOR'S CATTLE OR HOGS. WE WOULD BUTCHER THE ANIMALS, CURE THE MEAT, THEN SELL IT. AND I GUESS MOST EVERYBODY IN GREEN COUNTY KNOWS THE KIND OF THINGS WE GET UP TO. I WON'T LIE AND SAY I DIDN'T DO THEM. BUT THIS CHARGE I'M UP ON NOW, WITH THE WHITE FAMILY, WELL, I WOULDN'T DO ANYTHING LIKE THAT. I DID SUGGEST WE ROB THEM, BUT IT WAS SADLER AND BELL WHO KILLED THEM. AND THAT'S ALL I HAVE TO SAY ABOUT IT.

Todd came back that night to retrieve Simpson's pages. Reviewing them, he figured Simpson had probably left out more than he'd put in. As bad as he'd made himself look, Todd thought, it wasn't half as bad as he probably really was. Still, the local citizens were hungry for any news of the men they were sure had done these terrible murders.

Simpson's story ran in newspapers across the region the following day.

CHAPTER 61

THE TRIAL

The twelve local men of the jury were already sitting in the small courtroom in the courthouse, located in the town square of Greensburg. The sheriff and his deputy walked in holding Carrington Simpson by each arm. Simpson was in chains, hand and foot. The chains were removed when he sat down next to Samuel Spencer.

Samuel Spencer was Simpson's attorney and was legally bound to defend him. He didn't have to like him—and he didn't. In fact, when Simpson walked into the room, Spencer felt he was in the presence of evil. Spencer had been retired for years but on occasion took cases as a favor to someone, usually a friend who needed help in a land or livestock dispute. Judge Motely had asked him to represent Simpson, since no other attorney in the area wanted any part of it.

Spencer knew he was facing a guilty verdict. Personally, he would be glad of it. To carry out his professional duties, he had tried to get the trial moved to Adair County, where Simpson might find a more merciful jury, but he had been denied. Spencer dreaded the result of a guilty verdict in Green County, because he was sure Simpson would receive a public hanging there, something to which Spencer objected on moral grounds.

Isaac Gibbons was representing the state of Kentucky in prosecuting Simpson. He was taking no chances, since the original trial of Jason Bell and Pleasant Sadler had resulted in a hung jury back in June. Each accused the other of actually committing the murders, and both pointed fingers at Simpson, saying he was the ringleader. In the confusion, the jury was not able to reach a verdict. In November, however, Bell was tried separately and convicted. His sentencing was suspended until August of 1841, by which time Sadler had also been convicted. They were both sentenced to hang.

However, neither Bell nor Sadler reached the gallows. They shared a cell, and days before they were to hang, an argument broke out, with each accusing the other of getting them into this situation. Bell called Sadler's mother a whore, and with that, Sadler hit Bell with a blow that knocked him to the floor. Before Bell could recover, Sadler was on top of him, hitting him again and again, blood spurting everywhere. Bell was partially unconscious and was unable to defend himself. Sadler clasped his strong hands around Bell's neck and began to squeeze the life from him. He could not squeeze hard enough with his right hand, which had been injured by the punches he'd thrown, so he grabbed a pillow from the cot and placed it over Bell's face, holding it there tightly until all movement stopped. Jason Bell was dead.

Pleasant Sadler had already decided he would not go to the gallows in front of thousands of gawking people, that he would go out in his own way. So the evil Sadler tied a belt around his neck, attached the other end to the bars in the small window of his cell, and hanged himself.

And so, when Isaac Gibbons started his opening remarks to the jury, he had recently learned that two of the defendants were already dead. He used this new knowledge to his advantage in pointing out the conniving Simpson and how he had orchestrated the whole murder plot.

"Gentlemen," Gibbons began, "sitting in this courtroom this morning is a man responsible for the death of five innocent people: Lucinda White, her two sons, Mattie Kessler White, and her baby boy Will. They were murdered at his hands for goods worth less than one hundred dollars. Now there are two more victims of Carrington Simpson: Jason Bell and his stepson, Pleasant Sadler, who was just a young boy led astray by the man you see sitting in front of you."

Simpson showed no emotion. In fact, it seemed he had a tiny smirk on his face.

"By his own admission," Gibbons continued, "he was involved in this plot, and by testimony we have heard from the other two, he was not only involved, the whole thing was his idea. This man was responsible for the deaths—by brutal beating with a shovel—of an innocent family, including a baby two years old whom he decapitated with that shovel."

An angry murmur went through the courtroom, with occasional shouts of "Hang the son of a bitch!" and "Let's hang him right now!"

Judge Motely gave two sharp raps with his gavel, calling for order. When the voices died down, Isaac Gibbons said he was finished with his opening remarks.

Then Samuel Spencer rose and walked slowly to the jury box, feeling every bit of his sixty-eight years of age. He faced the people watching in the courtroom, and then he turned to face the jury.

"Gentlemen of the jury," he said, "what you have before you is not a monster but a victim of his upbringing. Carrington Simpson was lost in a family of seven brothers and sisters, all with different fathers, from a mother who never married. It led him to a life of self-interest and falling in with evil companions. Mr. Gibbons would like for you to come back with a quick verdict to hang this man, a war veteran. I ask you: what purpose would that serve?"

With that, he turned to face the audience again and saw Daniel Kessler sitting there. It completely threw him off his train of thought, and all he could think to say was, "Your Honor, that concludes my opening remarks."

With that, the judge called a recess until after lunch. Simpson was led back to his cell.

During the recess, Daniel was approached by several men, including one of his best friends, Rex Berle, who assured him, "Don't you worry, Daniel; he is going to hang."

His son Henry was there, too. He added, "Dad, every man on that jury knows you and knew Mattie and Will. They will make sure justice is done."

CHAPTER 62

TESTIMONY

When court resumed, Isaac Gibbons called his first witness, Regina Johnson.

"Mrs. Johnson, what is your occupation?" Gibbons asked.

"I'm a seamstress," she replied.

"Did you ever do any work for Lucinda White and her daughter-in-law Mattie White?"

"Yes, I did."

"Can you tell the court about that?"

"Objection, Your Honor," Samuel Spencer said. "What is the relevance of these questions? What does a dressmaker have to do with a murder trial?"

"Your Honor," Gibbons said, "if you will permit me to continue, I assure you there is a definite relevance."

"Objection overruled," the judge said. "You may answer the question, Mrs. Johnson."

"Lucinda and Mattie came to me a month or so before they were to leave on their trip to Alabama. They brought some very fine material that they had specially ordered through Mr. Kerry's general store. They wanted to know if I could make them each a dress before they left. I told them I thought I could but that I would need to get started right away. I finished the dresses in plenty of time, and they turned out real nice, especially Lucinda's, which had a special neckline with ruffled edges."

"Did you ever have an occasion to see that dress again?" asked Gibbons.

"Yes, but not on Lucinda White. When I saw it, it was being worn by a member of the Simpson family. I made sure it was the exact dress. I always put a special identifying mark on all my dresses, and I got really close to make sure it was mine."

Gibbons held up a dress.

"Is this the dress you saw?"

"Yes, it is. There is the lavender mark in the hem on the side. You have to look closely to see it."

"Your Honor, I would like to submit this dress as Exhibit A for the prosecution," Gibbons said. "Now, Mrs. Johnson: did you ever see the dress you made for Mattie?"

"No, but I would recognize it if I saw it. She probably never had a chance to wear it before she was raped and murdered by *him*," Regina said, pointing to Simpson.

"Objection, Your Honor!" Spencer bellowed.

"Sustained," Judge Motely said. "Mrs. Johnson, please refrain from offering opinions and only answer the questions asked."

Then it was time for Spencer's cross-examination.

"Mrs. Johnson, did you ever actually see Lucinda White or Mattie wearing the dresses you'd made them? I mean, after the dresses were fitted and left your shop?"

"No, sir."

"So it's possible Lucinda could have sold that dress before she left?" Spencer asked.

"Anything is possible, Mr. Spencer, but it's unlikely that a woman would sell a dress she'd just had made for herself."

"He's a thief and a murderer!" someone hollered from the audience.

Judge Motely again called the courtroom to order.

"I have no further questions, Your Honor," Spencer said.

"I only have one more witness, Your Honor," Gibbons said. "But I must warn you, this will be graphic testimony. The victims' families, as well as the public, should be warned, and all should be cautioned against outbursts."

The judge agreed and cautioned the courtroom.

"Your Honor," Gibbons said, "the state calls Dr. Stuart Wayne. Dr. Wayne, will you please state your full name and occupation?"

"My name is Dr. Stuart Wayne. I am a physician and state medical examiner for Green County and some of the surrounding counties."

"Were you present the night the bodies of the five victims involved in this trial were discovered?"

"Yes, I was."

"Can you tell the court what you saw and give your expert testimony on what happened to those bodies?"

"Certainly," the doctor replied. "We found the bodies in an old field on the Simpson farm. They were in a hole, covered slightly, principally with rotten tobacco stalks, the house having been previously a tobacco barn. When the bodies were exhumed, Lewis White was on top; next to him was Lucinda White. Then came John White and then the infant Will White, Daniel Kessler's grandson. At the bottom was Matilda Kessler White, wife of William.

"Although in a high state of putrefaction, the bodies could all be identified and recognized by those who had known them well. One was further identified by the comb in her hair and the ring upon her finger, another by her teeth and the color of her hair, another by the peculiarity of his teeth. It seems that all had their clothes removed before interment, except for Mattie, the daughter-in-law."

There was a long pause. The doctor's eyes were watering; he had helped in the deliveries of both Mattie and Will, had known them well.

"Take your time, Doctor," Gibbons said. "I know this must be difficult."

Dr. Wayne glanced up and saw Daniel sitting there, stoic, with his arms folded across his chest. Their eyes met and Daniel nodded ever so slightly, telling the doctor it was all right to continue.

"Mattie's clothing was pulled up over her head and her arms were tied above her head. From this, I assume she was abused and raped by the men before being brutally murdered. A rope was tied around her body. The skull of each person was fractured, in my estimation, all by the same instrument, except for the head of young Will, which was completely smashed and severed from his body."

His voice broke as he talked about the baby. He looked up at Daniel again and saw that Daniel was in tears, as were many in the audience.

"Hangin' is too good for that bastard Simpson!" shouted someone from the audience.

"No further questions, Your Honor," Gibbons said. "The state rests."

"There will be a thirty-minute break to give the defense time to prepare," the judge said.

"That may not be necessary, Your Honor," Spencer said. "if you will allow me to speak with you and Mr. Gibbons in your chambers right now."

In the judge's chambers, Spencer said, "I'm duty bound to serve my client, and I could call some defense witnesses, but anyone who would speak up for Simpson is as dirty and untrustworthy as he is. I think we all know what the outcome of this trial will be—and should be—regardless of what I do.

"My suggestion is this: I believe I can get a confession from Mr. Simpson, which would save us all from having to go through more of this and would save the families from having to endure it. If I can get a confession, Your Honor, will you consider recommending Simpson be given life in prison instead of the death penalty?"

"The state would not go along with that, Your Honor," Gibbons interrupted. "Simpson is a threat to society and is a heinous murderer who deserves no mercy."

The judge considered.

"I can give no guarantees about the sentencing. It's up to the jury," he said at last. "And I doubt they will be merciful, no matter what I recommend. However, if you can have Simpson's full confession to me when court begins tomorrow, I will promise him that if he does hang, he will have a decent burial and a headstone."

"I will see what I can do, Your Honor," Spencer said.

CHAPTER 63

THE CONFESSION

That night Spencer sat in the cell with Simpson and told him about the conversation with the judge. At first, Simpson didn't like the idea of confessing, but the more he thought about it . . . well, there was something he liked about getting all the attention and having his story told in the history books. Not only that, he still felt confident that he could figure a way out of this situation. *I always have*, he thought, smiling.

"All right, I'll do it," he said. "But I want a military headstone, telling people I served in the Second Infantry."

"I'm sure the judge will agree to that," Samuel said, pulling out pencil and paper.

"I also want some tobaccy and shine while I tell my story," Simpson said.

Spencer produced a tobacco pouch and handed it over, adding, "I'll bring you the booze after we're done. Let's get started."

Simpson pulled out a pipe, placed the tobacco between his thumb and forefinger, and stuffed his pipe with it.

"Match?" he asked.

Samuel handed him a wooden match.

Simpson lit the match on the side of the chair he was sitting in, put it to his pipe, and puffed until a white circle of smoke came from the pipe. He placed his hand over the pipe and took a long draw from it, then blew smoke out with a sigh of pleasure. He looked at Samuel and grinned.

"Lucinda White," Samuel reminded him.

"Yeah, Lucinda White . . ." Simpson said. "Lucinda was a resident of Green County and ran a tippling house that me and my friends frequented to buy beer. It wasn't really beer, because she used corn instead of hops, but it had a kick to it. And Lucinda had a recipe she made from persimmons; she bottled it in quart jars and sold it as cider. She could make a batch and it would only have to sit about two days before it fermented. She also had a couple of tables and chairs set up, in case customers would like to have some while they were there.

"On one such occasion, I was having a glass of that cider and started talking to one of her sons, and he informed me that his brother had gone to Alabama and that he and his other brother, along with their mama, were thinking of going there also. Lucinda had mentioned many times that she and her two sons, along with her daughter-in-law Mattie Kessler and Mattie's son, would like to go to Alabama. Mattie was the wife of William White. She wanted to be with her husband, whom she had not heard from for months. William was by no means in good with his father-in-law, Daniel Kessler, who strongly opposed Mattie going to Alabama.

"So even though we knew the women folk and their young 'uns

wanted to go, I didn't want to cross Old Man Kessler, so I never pursued it until one night I was drinking with my partners, Jason Bell and Pleasant Sadler. Jason Bell had a stillhouse about six miles out of Greensburg and four miles from me. It was a place where we would meet and drink and plan our next moneymaking scheme, mainly from cheating and stealing from others.

"That night, the subject came up of Lucinda White wanting somebody to move her and her family to Alabama. Sadler remarked that she had a purse as long as his arm. Then I said it would be a pretty good haul, assuming we would rob them. But Sadler then proposed to me and Bell that we should kill Lucinda and all the family and throw them in the river. Bell agreed to the killing but objected to throwing them in the river as the bodies would eventually be discovered and we could get caught. Bell asked me if I knew of a deep hole where they could dispose of the bodies. I told them of a suitable place nearby, an old potato hole in a waste house located in an old field of mine.

"We agreed that I would go to Lucinda's house and tell her that Bell, Sadler, and I would move them in five days for a fee of ten dollars a head and that she must be ready to start by Saturday night. I told her we'd need to leave at night due to Daniel Kessler's insistence that his daughter and grandson not go. I told her, 'He will be home on Saturday, and Mattie can tell him that she and the boy will be spending the night with you. By the time he realizes on Sunday that all of you are missing from church service, you will be well on your way to Alabama.' And she agreed.

"On Saturday night, we were at my place, ready to go at dusk with our ox team and wagon, when Mattie and her son appeared. I was standing outside. Bell and Sadler were in the house drinking. In fact, we had been drinking all afternoon. That Sadler boy gets meaner and meaner the more he drinks. He and Bell were already arguing about who would get what when we did the robbery. Sadler said the robbery was his idea, so he should have first pick. There was a pair of boots that one of those boys had that Sadler had his eye on . . ."

"As Mattie approached, she saw me and told me that she and the boy would not be going but that Lucinda and her son were waiting on us. I asked her what about the other son, and she told me that he had left a day or so earlier on horseback. Didn't want to wait and figured that he would meet them there.

"The fact that Mattie wasn't going didn't bother us. It was Lucinda White's money that we were after. But we had been drinking all day and decided to have a little fun with Mattie.

"I approached her and said, 'That's all right, Miss Mattie. Why don't you come in and have a beverage with us before starting your trip home?'

"She said, 'No, thanks. I should be going.'

"'Ah, come on,' I said. 'What is one little drink going to hurt?'

"'I said no, Mr. Simpson,' she said. 'Now if you will please turn loose of my horse, I will be on my way.'

"I told her, 'What, you think you're too good for us? Now, come on, Mattie, you have to be a little lonely for some manly company, being how your husband has been gone so long and is obviously not interested in taking care of you, staying in Alabama all this time.' Then I reached up and grabbed her around the waist and pulled her off the horse. She was holding the boy in one arm but swung around with the other and slapped me across the face. The boy was crying loud and Mattie was screaming at me to let her go.

"'Wait until my father and brother hear about this,' she said.

"At that time, Sadler came out and was mad as hell about all the noise, especially the boy crying. I told him I was going to have a little fun with Mattie and that he should take the boy out back for a while. He grabbed the boy, who was still crying loudly, and told him to shut up.

"I grabbed Mattie from behind, lifted her off her feet, and carried her inside. She was begging Sadler not to take the baby. She said he would stop crying if we just gave him back to her, that he was afraid. But Sadler took him on out back anyway.

"Then Bell came out and asked what was going on, and I told him he could join in the fun. Mattie was fighting, but I held her tight with her feet off the ground. We were joking and laughing when Bell walked over and lifted up Mattie's dress.

"'What do we have here?' he said, laughing. 'I often wondered what was underneath this dress of yours. Well, look here, Simpson, she looks just like all the whores at the stillhouse, when you get past all these fancy clothes. I guess you don't feel so prim and proper now, do you, bitch?' And then we tied her to the top of the table and pulled her dress and arms over her head and tied them too. She kept begging us to let her and the baby go, saying she would never tell what we had done. But we were too far into the deed to stop.

"We pulled down her undergarments and spread her legs and tied them to the table. I told Bell to go outside and check on Sadler and the boy. As Bell was walking out, he turned to Mattie and said, 'You ain't nothing but a common old dirt farmer's daughter. Guess you wasn't good enough to hold your man. Me and Simpson gonna find out real quick.'

"After I had my way with her, I went outside to check on the other two and see if they wanted some of the fun. I walked up on them about fifty yards from the house. It was very dark, but I could see Sadler standing there with a shovel, talking to Bell. I asked them who wanted to go next, and then I asked where the boy was. Sadler looked at me and motioned down the hill. I walked up to what was left of the boy. Sadler had hit him in the back of the head, then brought the blade down on his neck. Cut his head clean off.

"'That crying was driving me crazy,' he said.

"Bell told me to wait there; it was his turn with Mattie. In a little while, he came out and told Sadler, 'She's all yours. You been wanting to get back at Old Man Kessler since he turned you in for killing that boy.'

"When Sadler came out, he was carrying Mattie over his shoulder, her dress still pulled over her head and tied to her arms. Her face was bruised and bleeding. Sadler had obviously beat her. He was a mean man. Mattie was crying and begging to be taken to her boy. So Sadler carried her down to where he lay. He had an evil grin on his face. Then I heard her scream, 'Will! Oh, my God, what have you done to him?' Then I heard a loud thud and then another and another . . . and it was over.

"We had just killed Old Man Kessler's daughter and grandson, and now we had to finish the job with the White family."

Here Simpson paused. Spencer made note of the fact that he had seen no sense of guilt or remorse in Simpson's voice or expression.

His tone was cold and flat. In fact, he seemed to be enjoying telling the story.

Simpson continued, "We carried the two bodies to the potato hole and threw them in and then covered them with brush and tobacco stalks. Then it was getting late and we needed to get to Lucinda's house. We finished loading the oxcart, grabbed a jug of shine, and headed out.

"We arrived at the tippling house at the appointed time. Lucinda greeted us and told us that Mattie and the boy were not going. Of course, we pretended to be surprised.

"We had decided we needed to kill John first, as he was fairly good with a pistol. We called for him to come outside and help us with the loading of the wagon. John was only about sixteen but was fully grown. Me and Bell were standing by the wagon when he walked out, his pistol in the waistband of his trousers. Sadler came up behind him and hit him across the head with the shovel. John went to his knees but at the same time pulled his revolver and aimed it at us. But then Sadler hit him a second time, splitting his head completely open. He fell facedown in a pool of blood, but not before he got off one shot. It didn't hit any of us, but it warned Lucinda. John was probably already dead, but Sadler smashed that shovel across his head one more time, just to make sure.

"Me and Bell ran into the house, but Lucinda was nowhere to be found. We knew she couldn't have gone far, but we needed to find her quick and get back to my place. Bell found her hiding in the bushes. He walked her back at gunpoint to where she saw John and fell to her knees beside him. She was crying and screaming at us. Kept asking us why we had done it. And then, without warning, Sadler brought that shovel down on the back of her head, knocking her to the ground. She moaned a little, and then he hit her again and then one more time.

"We threw both bodies on the cart and took them to the waste house and threw them in the same hole with Mattie and her child. The cart was then loaded with Lucinda's worldly goods, which were carried off to my place, where the division of the spoils took place.

"The next day, Lewis, Lucinda's son who had started off beforehand on the old gray horse, returned, alleging that the horse was about to give out, that he was satisfied that it could never perform the trip, and that he had concluded to leave the old horse and travel with the rest of the family. Arriving at Lucinda's house, he had found it vacant, and he supposed they had started on their trip and that he had missed them along the way. He hunted up Sadler, who prevailed upon him to conceal himself until dark so Old Man Kessler would not see him and start asking questions about his daughter going to Alabama. Sadler convinced him to hide himself in the old barn until night. Later that night, Sadler led him into the old field and beat him with an ax handle until dead. He then deposited his body in the same hole with the others. He made sure he removed those boots, though, before depositing his body.

"I should also mention that the poor old gray horse was also taken to the old field and killed near the waste house so that we could explain any disagreeable smells which might arise from the decomposing bodies. They would be attributed to the carcass of the dead horse, which Sadler killed in the same manner as he had Lewis. He could have just shot them both, but I guess he wanted to beat them with that ax handle."

"Unlike the gray horse that was too old to sell, Mattie's horse, Good Fellow, was in good shape and would be easy to turn a profit with. A good riding horse is valuable to travelers heading west. We had such people coming through the stillhouse regularly. We had to be careful, though, because her horse was known by some of the locals, plus we couldn't be seen around the stillhouse. We were supposed to be on the road to Alabama.

"We decided to solicit the help of one of the girls, Cookie. We knew that a good riding horse is worth at least seventy-five dollars. We told her to talk to J. T., one of her customers, who we knew was traveling to Virginia and needed a good horse. We had him meet us out by the old barn, where he could see the horse. He was leaving for Virginia early the next morning, so the deal was easily made for thirty-five dollars, and he agreed not to tell anybody where he got the horse. We gave Cookie five dollars for helping us and we took ten apiece, a pretty good haul.

"After five days, Bell and I returned, and everyone, including Old Man Kessler, assumed we had moved the White family to Alabama."

With that, Carrington Simpson's story was told. Spencer stowed away his notebook and pen and wordlessly left the jail. He procured a bottle of shine and brought it back to the jail, leaving it with the deputy; he would be true to his word in providing it, but he did not want to see Simpson again that night.

Heavyhearted, he went home in the knowledge that at least the confession would bring the trial to a close and let the White and Kessler families grieve in peace.

CHAPTER 64

THE VERDICT

The trial started on time the next morning at nine o'clock sharp. Judge Motely called on Spencer, and Spencer handed to the court clerk his handwritten pages from the night before. The judge reviewed them as the people in the audience shifted uneasily in their seats.

Finally, Judge Motely set down the papers and addressed the jury.

"Gentlemen," he said, "The defense will not be presenting a case to you. These papers contain a full confession from the defendant, Mr. Simpson. This will be added as an exhibit to the trial, along with the two dresses and the shovel. I encourage you to examine them all carefully and to review what you have heard in this courtroom. The outcome of this trial—and of this tragedy—is now in your hands. You have two decisions to make, and both must be unanimous.

"The first decision is whether the defendant is innocent or is guilty beyond a reasonable doubt. If your first decision is one of guilt, then it is incumbent upon you to determine the defendant's sentence, either life in prison or death by hanging. If no unanimous decision can be reached concerning the sentencing, then the court will decide for you. But you must do your best to see that justice is done for all involved. You may now retire to the jury room, where your foreman, Mr. Marshall, will lead you in the process."

The jury deliberated for less than two hours. Simpson's confession had skirted the issue of his involvement in the actual murders, but the jury wasn't fooled. They knew the whole plan had been his idea, as were all the exploits of Simpson, Sadler, and Bell. If not for Carrington Simpson, the White family would still be alive; it was as simple as that. The deliberation would have been even shorter, but one juror favored life in prison over death by hanging. But other jurors told him surely Simpson would kill again if given the chance, and eventually he agreed. They returned to the courtroom.

"Gentlemen," Judge Motely asked, "have you reached a verdict?"

"Yes, Your Honor," Marshall said.

"Please hand the verdict to the clerk," the judge directed.

The clerk read out the verdicts in a clear voice that carried easily over the hushed courtroom.

"On the charge of first-degree murder of Lucinda White, we find the defendant guilty. On the charge of first-degree murder of John White, we find the defendant guilty. On the charge of first-degree murder of Lewis White, we find the defendant guilty. On the charge of first-degree murder of the baby Will White, we find the defendant guilty. On the charges of torture, rape, and first-degree murder of Matilda Kessler White, we find the defendant guilty.

"It is the recommendation of this jury that the sentence be death by hanging."

Judge Motely polled the jury, and one by one they confirmed their verdicts and sentencing. Then he asked Simpson to rise.

"It is the finding of this court that you are guilty of brutally murdering five innocent people and of the torture and rape of one as well. Therefore, in accordance with the jury's recommendation, I am sentencing you to death by hanging. The sentence is to be carried out at noon on the twenty-first day of September, 1841. May God have mercy on your soul.

"This court is adjourned."

CHAPTER 65

JUSTICE

As Carrington Simpson lay in his cell, he could hear the banging of hammers from the newly constructed town square. He knew it was the gallows—his gallows—but Simpson had always been able to get out of a jam, and he thought maybe he could do it this time. He still had plenty of money from the robbery of Lucinda and from other robberies; maybe he could bribe Sheriff Willy and escape. No one would blame Willy; he would just be an old man who forgot to lock the cell.

Simpson offered Willy five hundred dollars if he would do just that.

"I could sure use that money," Willy said, "for my retirement, which is fast approaching. This is my last case. I can't leave the cell unlocked, but if I happened to drop the key, accidentally, where you could reach it . . ."

"That will work just fine," Carrington said, "but how do I know I can trust you?"

"You are gonna hang if you don't trust me," Willy said.

Simpson figured he had nothing to lose, so he told Willy where the money was hidden, out at the stillhouse. He had only given Bell and

Sadler a fraction of the takings: their share of the hundred dollars they thought had been in Lucinda's purse and of the money earned from the sale of the party's clothes and Mattie's horse. They'd had no idea of the valuable articles of jewelry, some with diamonds, and several gold pieces that Simpson had pocketed while Sadler and Bell were disposing of the bodies. Bell and Sadler drank their money up and used it on whores; Simpson had saved most of his for just such an occasion as this.

That night Simpson heard a metal tinkling sound: a key hitting a wood floor. He smiled and thought how he would be long gone out of the county by morning. He knew he could steal a horse, what with all the people in town for the hanging. His plan was to ride through the night to the Ohio River and board a flatboat to Missouri. He knew they would probably look for him to head to Virginia or Ohio.

He heard Willy say good night to the half-wit deputy who watched the place during the night, and then he heard the door close behind Willy.

Mostly the deputy slept, but once every night he would slip out and head down to the town square to visit a saloon. Simpson decided he would make his break then.

In the meantime, Willy rode out to the stillhouse and talked to Ginger, whom he had known for years. They had a good relationship, mainly because old Willy always looked the other way when it came to Ginger's whores. So when he told her he wanted one of the girls and wanted the back room, she obliged. She was surprised; it had been a long time since Willy had come calling for one of the girls. She had thought he'd gotten too old.

After they got to the room, Willy told the girl to wait outside. He would call her in when he was ready. Simpson had told him there was a loose board under the bed near the wall. Willy took out his long-bladed knife to pry it up. The first board did not budge. Willy tried another; still no luck. On the third try, though, his knife slid easily between the boards and the slat popped up. Willy raised the board, reached in, and took out a heavy canvas sack. He knew it was the stolen money.

He walked out of the room, handed the girl a lot more money than she would ordinarily make in a night, and told her he wouldn't be needing her services and to keep quiet on how much he had paid her. The girl didn't understand, but she was grateful that she'd just earned a good sum of money without having to sleep with a stinking old dried-up sheriff.

It was a good night for all except one.

After hearing the deputy open and close the door to go get his drink at the saloon, Carrington rolled out of bed. He walked to the front of the cell and saw the key lying on the floor . . . just out of his reach.

That dumb old bastard, he thought.

He took off his boot and forced it through the bars, then reached his arm through, trying to move as fast as he could before the deputy came back. With the boot as an extension to his arm, he was able to reach the key. He couldn't get his boot back through the bars, but it didn't matter; soon he would be on the other side. It was a hot September night and Simpson was drenched in sweat, but his plan was working. He smiled and thought, *They can't hold Carrington Simpson*. He considered himself invincible. He reached around the door, stuck the key into the lock, and turned it.

Nothing happened.

He tried again. Still nothing. He turned the key upside down. Nothing. He turned it again and shook the door. Nothing.

"I'm going to kill that old bastard!" Simpson hollered.

Then he heard a voice above him.

"You've done all the killing you're ever gonna do."

Simpson looked up and saw Sheriff Willy standing in the doorway. Simpson knew he had been had by an old "burned-out" sheriff.

That afternoon, Samuel Spencer came to see him.

"Carrington," Samuel said, "you are going to meet your maker tomorrow at high noon. Just to let you know, the judge is living up to his end of the bargain and will provide you with a gravesite and a headstone denoting that you were a veteran. I think you should know, though, that you won't be buried in a regular cemetery with ordinary folks. You will be buried in a field, by yourself, near the community of Grab, about four miles outside of town.

"That's the best I could do for you, Simpson. Most folks think it is more than you deserve."

Simpson did not respond . . .

CHAPTER 66

THE SHORT DROP

As many as ten thousand people converged on the small town of Greensburg, Kentucky, on the morning of September 21, 1841, to watch the execution of Kentucky's most notorious murderer, Carrington Simpson. Many came in horse-drawn wagons: couples, families, ranchers, and travelers who were just passing through.

The party had gone on for two days now. There were bands playing, street vendors, preachers, and healers all selling something. There was a lot of drinking, of course. The army had a tent set up for recruiting young men, with many getting drunk and enlisting.

Ginger's girls from the stillhouse were recruiting the young men, too. They had set up quarters in a wagon outside of town. They worked the saloon to pick up men, then walked the men to the outskirts of town and serviced them in the wagon. Ginger was close by, making sure she received her cut and that nothing happened to the girls. Sheriff Willy had warned her not to conduct any business inside the town, but otherwise, he looked the other way.

Altogether, it was quite a celebration. Nothing close to this big had ever happened in Greensburg or in Green County.

The hangman, James B. Montgomery, had finished his work preparing the gallows; he would charge five dollars for the hanging and one dollar for the rope. In 1841, all hangings were either done by lynching or by the "short drop." Hangings inside the law were all done with the short drop. This method involved a gallows with stairs leading up to a platform. On the platform was a wooden bracket which provided support for the rope and the body. There was no trap door. The prisoner stepped up onto a stool or a small ladder; the noose was then slipped around the neck and the stool was kicked away. The prisoner would die a slow death by strangulation.

Although the short drop was more humane than an illegal lynching, it had other complications. The blood would be cut off to the brain but would gush to other parts of the body, including the genitals. In men, it would sometimes engorge the penis, creating an erection for all to see. It would be a slow, painful, humiliating death for Carrington Simpson.

At eleven o'clock, Sheriff Willy and two deputies appeared at his cell.

"It's time, Simpson," Willy said.

"You screwed me and stole my money!" Simpson shouted.

"He's talking like a madman," Willy said calmly to his deputies.

"No matter," said Jake, the older of the two. "He will need more than money where he's heading."

The younger deputy held a rifle on Simpson as Willy opened the cell door.

"Turn around and put your hands high on the wall," Willy told him.

When they got inside the cell, they lowered Simpson's hands behind his back and tied them there. A belt about three feet long was attached to his hands and held by Jake, who was a big, stout man.

The gallows was about two hundred yards from the jail, but Simpson could see it as soon as he walked outside. He walked toward the gallows with Jake behind him, holding the belt much as if he were walking a dog, and Willy and the young deputy on either side of him. The deputy had a rifle, and Willy had a double-barreled shotgun.

Simpson showed no emotion, but the back of his shirt was soaked with sweat. It was now eleven-thirty, and they were about a hundred yards away from the hanging place. At one point, Simpson felt his legs buckle; he was now sweating profusely.

He told Willy, "I need to piss."

"Too late," Willy said. "You are out of time."

They continued to walk, and the closer to the gallows they got, the more Simpson began to slouch. His gait was much smaller now, so Willy grabbed his arm and moved with him to both hold him up and keep him moving. Jeers and cheers were coming from the crowd; some had signs held up in the air with sticks and boards. Many of the signs simply read MURDERER; some read BABY KILLER or BURN IN HELL.

Willy was getting nervous. He was worried the crowd would get out of hand. Many were already drunk. They could easily turn into a lynch mob. He continued to push his way through the crowd; it was slow going. One man in the crowd threw a punch at Simpson but was warded off by the young deputy. Most men there knew not to mess with Jake; not only was he a strong, tough character who had done prizefighting when he was younger, but he was likely to be the new sheriff after this was over.

It took them almost ten minutes to walk the final hundred yards. By then, Simpson was barely standing on his own. They reached the bottom of the stairs. Simpson looked up and saw James B. Montgomery, the hangman, who wore a mask. He held a hood to place over Simpson's head. Blocking the foot of the stairs was another man. When Simpson looked up to see who it was, there stood Daniel Kessler.

Daniel stood there for ten or fifteen seconds, staring down at the shrunken Carrington Simpson, the man who had murdered his daughter and grandson. The men just looked at each other, saying nothing. Then Willy nudged Simpson to move on up. As Willy passed Daniel, he placed his hand on the top of Daniel's shoulder and gave him a squeeze. Daniel's emotions were running wild; he felt love from Willy but hatred toward Simpson.

When they reached the top of the stairs, Simpson was asked whether he had any last words, but he was defiant to the end.

"I don't need that hood," he shouted, "and I want all you all to know Sheriff Willy screwed me out of my money."

With that, the hangman placed the rope around Simpson's neck and tightened the noose so it would not slip. He then placed a stool on the platform and told Simpson to step on the stool. The young deputy tied a rope around Simpson's legs at the ankles, tightly securing them.

At noon exactly, James Montgomery pulled the stool out from under Simpson, letting his body drop the short distance of about six inches. The noose immediately started tightening around Simpson's neck. His body writhed as the noose did its work, cutting off the windpipe and slowly strangling the notorious murderer. The way Montgomery had purposely tied the knot assured that the airway would be constricted in a certain way that would initially be excruciating as Simpson struggled for air against the compression of the noose and his own body weight.

After about five minutes, Simpson's brain began to die. The blood normally going to the brain was now pooling under the skin. The pressure of blood was mounting and mounting until the capillaries in his face and eyes started to burst. The heart was barely beating, but death came slowly. It would depend on which organ gave out first.

Ten minutes in, Simpson was hardly moving. Foam was running from his mouth and his pants were soaked with urine. And then the final humiliation: what was known as the "death erection."

The hangman waited ten more minutes, until there was no movement at all, and then he pronounced Carrington Simpson dead.

As he stared at the body of Simpson, Daniel thought: *This is not enough.* Nothing would ever be enough; no amount of justice could ever replace Mattie and Will. No revenge or retribution could ever replace the joy of laughter from his daughter and the playfulness of a two- year-old baby.

He was glad that Eve did not have to live this nightmare; her hurt would have been unbearable. He thought, *I am ready to join them.*

CHAPTER 67

AFTER THE HANGING

The body of Carrington Simpson hung in the town square of Greensburg for hours after his death. Thousands of people walked by, staring at the state's most infamous murderer. From old to young they paraded by, some mocking, some spitting at him, but mostly they just stared, wanting to see what he looked like. Even young mothers with little children paraded by, some trying to shield the children's eyes, but to no avail: the children wanted to see.

Right before dusk, Sheriff Willy and his deputies cut the body down. A wooden coffin was ready, and they placed the body inside and nailed it shut. They placed the coffin on a wagon and took it out to Grab, where there was a graveyard and a church on one side of the road and a vacant field on the other side. Simpson's grave had been dug in the field, a good two hundred yards away from the road and church. The site was located under a tree. There was a white, railed cage fence surrounding the grave.

The coffin was lowered into the ground and covered with dirt, without ceremony. There was a white headstone, as the judge had promised. Toward the top was a cross with a circle around it. The engraving read:

CARRINGTON SIMPSON

Pvt 1 Va. Regiment Militia

War of 1812

Aug. 10 1782–Sept. 21 1841

Nothing appeared on the stone about his murderous deeds. The judge had fulfilled his promise to Simpson that if he cooperated with a confession, he could have a decent burial. Anyone seeing this stone in the field outside Greensburg, Kentucky, would think it was just an ordinary veteran buried there. Simpson's wife Dicey would also be buried there when she died in 1880 at age ninety.

Only one man, other than the men of the burial detail, was at the single-grave cemetery that day. Standing about thirty yards away was the daunting figure of big Daniel Kessler.

Daniel could not help but think about how Mattie and young Will had suffered at the hands of this butcher lying in the ground with a military headstone. His Mattie and Will were buried in the same box together. He turned, with tears in his eyes, and headed for home.

CHAPTER 68

MAKING AMENDS

Three months passed. Daniel's son Henry had all but taken over the responsibilities of the farm. Daniel kept mostly to himself.

It was a sunny December morning, warm enough for Daniel to sit on his front porch after breakfast to enjoy a cup of coffee and puff on his corncob pipe. Mostly, these days, he would just sit and stare and reminisce about the early days when he and Ulrich had first traveled to Kentucky. He thought of Eve and how much he had loved her, about the joy and hardships in their lives, about their children, and especially about Mattie and Will.

His eyes strained to see a rider who appeared in the distance. As the rider got closer, it was apparent that he was heading toward the house and that another horse was trotting alongside his. Daniel went inside and got his double-barreled gun. His eyes were weak, and the rider had to get very close to the house before Daniel could recognize him. Daniel was standing now, holding his shotgun with one hand and bracing it across his other arm. The gun was loaded and cocked.

"Morning, Daniel," Sheriff Willy said.

"Morning, Sheriff. What brings you out this way?" Daniel asked, with skepticism.

"First of all, I'm no longer the sheriff," Willy said. "My retirement was final last week."

"So again, I say, what brings you out here?"

"Daniel, I hope you can hear me out before you run me off your land. I have a powerful sorrow in my heart over what happened to Mattie and Will. There hasn't been an hour gone by since the hanging that I didn't think of them and how maybe if I had run those three vermin out of the county, Mattie and Will would be with us today. I knew your father, Daniel, and I know he was a strong man, but he was also a forgiving man. As you know, he died peacefully in Ohio with his daughter by his side. His wish for you was that your life would not be as hard as his, and I know he instilled his forgiving nature into you and would want you to live your remaining years in peace, not bitterness.

"What I'm about to tell you, only two people on this earth will know about: me and you. I couldn't say anything as long as I was sheriff, but now I'm retired.

"On the night before the hanging, Simpson made me a proposition that he would give me five hundred dollars in cash if I would help him escape. I told him I would. I never intended to keep my end of the bargain, but I wanted to get my hands on that money that he and the other two snakes had stolen from innocent people. So I got him to tell me where the money was. Here is that money, Daniel, and I want you to have it."

Willy paused as he held out the canvas bag. He could tell by the expression on Daniel's face and the tears in his eyes that he was moved.

"I don't want the money," Daniel said. "It's blood money."

"It's not blood money or charity, Daniel. No man on Earth could say they earned the money more than you," Willy said as he placed the money next to Daniel.

Daniel paused for a long moment.

"Still some coffee on the stove, if you care for a cup," he said.

"Don't mind if I do," Willy replied. He walked inside the house and poured himself a cup of strong, black coffee.

"Daniel, you still make the strongest pot of coffee in the county. You could float a horseshoe in this," Willy quipped.

"Way I like it."

"There are a couple of other things, Daniel," Willy said. "I wasn't sure about this, but you might be wondering why I traveled out here with two horses. After the hanging, a man came to me and said he knew where Mattie's horse was . . ."

Daniel looked at Willy and then at the other horse.

"Is that Good Fellow?" he asked.

"Yep, sure is, Daniel. He is a couple of years older now but still in good shape. I knew Mattie would be happy to know he was home with you."

Daniel stepped off the porch and walked over to the horse. "Hello, boy," he said as he rubbed Good Fellow's head and ears.

Willy got back on his mount.

"I need to be heading back now, Daniel," he said. "There is just one other thing. There was a box under the bed at the stillhouse, where the money was hidden. You have all the money now; the boys in town pitched in and bought Good Fellow back. The only other thing in the box was this. Thought maybe you might want it."

Willy handed Daniel an object wrapped in a piece of cloth.

Daniel unwrapped the cloth and stared at the object. He said nothing, but he felt his knees weakening as he sat down on the porch. As Willy rode off, Daniel's head sagged, and he cried as he looked at the old army knife in his hands.

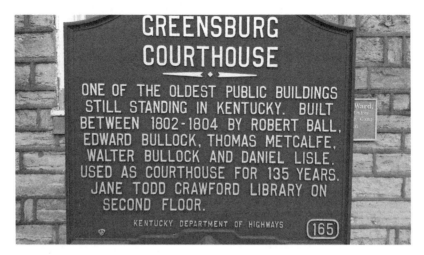

This plaque is located in front of the former Green County courthouse, where Carrington Simpson's trial took place in 1841.

The old courthouse, which dates from 1802, still stands in the Downtown Greensburg Historic District.

This historic building in Greensburg may have been the jail where Carrington Simpson, Jason Bell, and Pleasant Sadler were held.

The old courthouse, sometimes called the Historic Greensburg Courthouse, served its original purpose until 1931, when a more modern courthouse was built.

EPILOGUE

A few days later, Daniel's son Henry rode up to the house where he'd been raised. The house had originally been built as a simple log cabin for Daniel and Eve, and each year, Daniel had added on to it. As he looked at the house, Henry thought how big it was for just one person.

He dismounted, tied his horse to one of the rings on the post outside, and walked toward the porch. There he saw his father asleep in the rocker, wearing the same clothes he'd had on when Henry had last seen him, two days before. Henry saw an exhausted old man; his father had aged so much in the past two years. The whole family had suffered from the tragedy, but there was no doubt Daniel had suffered the most. He was no longer the upright, square-shouldered, strapping specimen of a man Henry had known as a boy, the man who had been known for his strength and his ability to outwork a man half his age.

Henry knew his father needed taking care of now. He had come to talk with Daniel about exactly that.

As Henry walked up the porch stairs, Daniel awoke with a start at the squeak of the boards.

"Sorry, Pa, didn't mean to wake you," Henry said. "Just wanted to drop off this food that Eliza prepared for you. I also wanted to talk to you, if you feel up to it."

"I'm awake now, Henry," Daniel said. "What's on your mind?"

"Well, Pa, me and Eliza have been thinking that it might be time for us to move into the big house here with you. As you know, she is about to have our third baby, and we don't have room for another at our place. You wouldn't have to be by yourself. Eliza would take care of the house, and you, me, and my boys could take care of the farm."

"What about the other house, the one you are in now? Who's going to take care of it and farm the ten acres over there?" Daniel asked.

"I know a young couple, just starting out, who are looking for a place to live and could pay us rent and share in the crops," Henry replied. "What do you think, Pa?"

As usual, no one could ever know what Daniel was thinking, especially when it came to business matters.

"Care for some coffee, son?" he asked.

"Yeah, Pa, I'll have a cup," Henry said, thinking, *This is a good sign. At least he didn't say no outright.*

"How's the tobacco looking?" Daniel asked. "Stripping will start in about a month."

Henry knew better than to say any more about the house; he had said enough. His father was not a man to be pushed.

"The tobacco is looking good, Pa," he said. "It's going to be a good year."

The two men sat in silence as they sipped their coffee. To Henry, it seemed like an eternity.

Finally, Daniel looked up into Henry's eyes and said, "Henry, I always figured you would be taking over the farm someday. I think your plan will suit me just fine."

Within a month, the family was together in the big house, and the house was alive again. Henry and Eliza shared a room with their newborn baby boy. Their older sons, Eunice and Zachary, shared another room. And Daniel still had his own.

Two weeks later, the new baby would be christened at the farm. It would be a simple ceremony with the preacher, some of Henry and Eliza's friends, the two older boys, and Daniel.

As everyone gathered around, Henry and Eliza carried the baby up to the preacher. Daniel, the godfather, came with them.

The baby had not been named yet, so the preacher asked, "What is the name you have given this boy?"

They both smiled at Daniel, and Eliza gently placed the baby into his arms.

"His name is Ulrich Daniel Kessler," Henry said.

Daniel's eyes filled with tears of joy, but he smiled, the first smile his family had seen from him in many months.

"Thank you," he said quietly. And then he gazed down into his new grandson's eyes, the same deep blue-green color as the sea that the first Ulrich had crossed so long before with his own family, all of them in search of the American dream.

To the Reader

Indentured: A Pathway to America is a book of historical fiction. Some of it is drawn from actual events; some is purely the imagination of the authors. Many of the characters were real, such as Johann and Matilda Kessler, along with their children Ulrich and his sister, although we do not know her real name. We do know that Matilda died at sea on the voyage to America, but we have little information concerning Johann. He may have died in America, or he may actually have gone back home. He, Ulrich, and the girl we have called Hannah were sold separately on auction blocks upon their arrival in America. There is nothing to tell us that they ever saw one another again. Mr. Steiner, Dutch, and the events on the farm are all fiction.

Ulrich did serve for eleven years as an indentured servant and then became a weaver. We think, though we cannot be certain, that Ulrich did live in or around Germantown, which was an established settlement by then. In 1683, a group of Mennonites, Pietists, and Quakers in Frankfurt, Germany, had approached Francis Pastorius, a renowned lawyer, educator, and public official from a prosperous Lutheran family, about acting as their agent to purchase land in Pennsylvania for a settlement. He had purchased fifteen thousand acres from William

Penn and laid out the settlement of Germantown. Pastorius was the first citizen of Germantown, becoming its mayor and serving in the Pennsylvania General Assembly. He lived in Germantown until his death in 1720.

The events concerning Ulrich and his family in Germantown and Lancaster, along with the events of the war, are all fiction, though of course the towns and the war are real. Many of the facts were taken from the history of that time, from magazine articles, history books, the internet, and other sources.

We do know and can track the latter part of Ulrich's story. He and his wife Anna had seven children; only the names of five could be found. We know he traveled from Pennsylvania with his family and settled for a while in Virginia and North Carolina. He and his sons—we're not sure how many—then migrated to Kentucky. Ulrich went on to Ohio after traveling with his son Daniel to Kentucky. He died there and is buried in Montgomery County.

Daniel did marry a woman named Eve, and they raised nine children on their two-hundred-acre Adair County farm on Sulphur Creek. The youngest of these children was Mattie, whose real name was Matilda after her great-grandmother. The murders, sadly, are a true story. The authors have expanded on this story here; some details of how the murders happened are fictionalized. But the five victims of the murder were indeed beaten to death with shovels, and Will, the baby, actually was decapitated. The total worth of the goods stolen was less than one hundred dollars.

Carrington Simpson, Jason Bell, and Pleasant Sadler were all real. The account of Simpson's confession is true but was rewritten to fit the narrative of the story. Simpson did confess to Samuel Spencer, his attorney; in return, he received a formal burial and a headstone with an inscription of his military service. The grave can still be found in the Grab area of Greensburg, Kentucky.

Simpson was hanged in the public square, but the account in the story is fiction. However, it is based on actual hangings of that time. Liberties were also taken with Bell and Sadler's deaths, but it is thought that Sadler did kill his stepfather, and we know he later hanged himself.

Daniel died in November of 1841, probably of a broken heart. His son Henry bought the land after Daniel's death and continued to farm it with his family.

Acknowledgments

We feel gratitude to so many people.

Larry's sister Kathleen did an excellent job on the genealogy of the Kessler family, and she must be first in line for a "thank you."

Certainly, we want to recognize Richard Taylor, English professor at Transylvania University. Richard went through the original manuscript and corrected many, many grammar and spelling errors. He also gave us suggestions on how to make the story read better.

The people at the Carnegie Center in Lexington, like Maddy Hamilton, were a great resource of information and were very helpful to a couple of fledgling writers. It was Maddy who put us in touch with Sarah Combs and her excellent class on how to write a scene.

Carol Butler of Butler Books was an immense help in guiding us.

Susan Lindsey, owner of Savvy Communication, gave us valuable editing coaching out of the goodness of her heart. In fact, we started over and changed the book's point of view due to her observations.

We can't say enough good things about our editor, Sarah Jane Herbener of Savvy Communication. She has diligently gone through our manuscript and given us guidance on how to improve it. Her grasp of the story and of what we were trying to accomplish with it was astonishing. She provided counsel on what she felt was best, but she allowed us to disagree. Her passion for excellence is obvious; hopefully, we will meet again on our next novel.

QUESTIONS WE HAVE
BEEN ASKED

1. How did the book come about?

Larry's sister Kathy, after whom Dutch's wife Kathleen was named, researched the genealogy of the Kessler family back in 1995. It started with Ulrich and how he came to America as an indentured servant at ten years of age. In the information she gathered was an excerpt from William B. Allen's wonderfully named 1872 book *A History of Kentucky: Embracing Gleanings, Reminiscences, Antiquities, Natural Curiosities, Statistics, and Biographical Sketches of Pioneers, Soldiers, Jurists, Lawyers, Statesmen, Divines, Mechanics, Farmers, Merchants, and Other Leading Men, of All Occupations and Pursuits*. The story of Mattie's and Will's murders was in that book, and it sparked our interest in putting our family's story into book form. We knew it had to be mostly fictionalized, because for the most part, all the information we had was names and dates.

We also felt the story of indentured servitude needed to be told.

2.   Was there a lot of research?

Yes, there was an enormous amount of research, covering almost one hundred years, four countries, five states, and five generations. Of course, some of the family research had already been done by Kathy, but the two of us extensively researched the time periods and the treatment of indentured people. Most of our research was done on Google, but we read through many books and magazines as well. We also visited the library and town hall in Greensburg and learned a lot there. The librarians and staff of the Green County Public Library were very helpful.

3.   How did you manage to work together?

Let's just say it was not easy. We don't recommend it, and neither of us will do it again.

4.   Who are some of your favorite authors, and what books have inspired you recently?

We both read constantly. We've particularly enjoyed and learned from:

The Nightingale and *Winter Garden*, Kristin Hannah

Where the Crawdads Sing, Delia Owens

Lilac Girls, Martha Hall Kelly

Me Before You, Jojo Moyes

Pat Conroy's historical fiction

Bill O'Reilly's "Killing" historical nonfiction series

Suggested Book Club Questions

1. This time in America was difficult, with the French and Indian War, the Revolutionary War, struggle, and poverty. Why do you think people still immigrated to America?

2. Do you think the Kesslers would still have made the decision to emigrate had they known of the conditions on the boat and of what awaited them in America?

3. Which characters did you like most?

4. Which characters did you dislike most?

5. Which characters did you relate to most? Why?

6. If this book were made into a movie, who would play Ulrich as a boy, as a young man, as an older man? Who would play Mr. Steiner, Dutch, Dolf, Anna, Daniel, Eve, Mattie, and Hannah?

7. Who would play Pleasant Sadler, Jason Bell, and Carrington Simpson?

About the Authors

Larry Kessler is a retired executive from Pitney Bowes, where he worked for thirty years. During those years, he lived mostly in Brentwood, Tennessee, but he has also lived in Ohio, Michigan, Maine, Georgia, Virginia, and Florida. While at Pitney Bowes, he won numerous national awards and eventually became in charge of all postal and sales training for North American operations. He now resides in Louisville, Kentucky, having moved back there after forty-six years away so that he and Maggie could live close to their quadruplet grandchildren. Larry and Maggie have seven grandchildren; the other three are in Chattanooga.

He holds a bachelor's degree from Eastern Kentucky University in education and attended Virginia Polytechnic Institute. He completed corporate classes at the University of Virginia's Darden Graduate School of Business. He served on the board of directors for the Tennessee Better Business Bureau.

When Larry is not writing or doing charitable work with a number of organizations, you will find him at the YMCA or on the golf course.

Larry and his wife of more than fifty years, Maggie, decided late in life to write a book together.

Maggie is an accomplished artist who majored in art at the University of Kentucky and has won several awards for her work in watercolors, oils, and acrylics. Her paintings have been featured in many art shows in Nashville. Some were displayed for years in the York & Friends gallery. Her art was also displayed by HGTV in a "giveaway" home in Nashville. One of her award-winning paintings hung in the House of Representatives in Washington, DC, for a year.

Maggie is also an excellent decorator and was at one time an avid tennis player and gardener. Today, she loves focusing on her seven grandchildren. In co-writing this book, which Maggie describes as a "journey," she has also discovered a passion for writing. Maggie has already started her next novel . . . without Larry.